Questioning Einstein

Is Relativity Necessary?

Tom Bethell

ii

Library of Congress Control Number: 2009923278

Tom Bethell
Questioning Einstein: Is Relativity Necessary

Includes bibliographic references
ISBN   10-digit: 0-9714845-9-7
            13-digit: 978-0-971-48459-7
1. Relativity
2. Michelson-Morley
3. Michelson-Gale

Printed in the USA
Cover design by Brian Dunbar

Cover photos from http://hubblesite.org. Material from Space Telescope Science Institute (STScI) prepared under NASA contract NAS5-26555

Vales Lake Publishing, LLC
P.O. Box 7609
Pueblo West, CO 81007-0609
SAN: 2 5 4—2 5 3

Acknowledgments

My principal debt is to Howard Hayden. Without his willingness to answer my questions, I would not have been able to finish this book. In fact, I would not have been able to start it. Petr Beckmann had shown me the big picture, but at his death there were hundreds of details that I needed to discuss, and understand. I believe that only Howard Hayden could have played that role, because he, perhaps uniquely, understood both Petr's argument and the opposing orthodoxy. It was fortunate indeed that Petr had brought Howard around to his point of view. I doubt if anyone else could have filled in for him; not just in encouraging me, but in strengthening Petr's own case with additional physical facts, arguments and details.

I soon learned that very few physicists are inclined to debate these issues. It's not that they are unwilling to talk to a layman. The problem is that, where Einstein's relativity is concerned, they have been trained to disregard all dissenting views. Only the strictest orthodoxy is allowed. Physics Ph.D.'s will have taken a relativity course, learned the Lorentz Transformations and so on. But the theory's premises won't be questioned. If new recruits to the academy pursue an academic career, they won't be open to any dissent or doubt about special relativity. Inconsistent experimental results will somehow lie outside their field of vision.

Still, I have reached a number of professional physicists, usually through the air waves. (Should I call it the ether?) Among them, a few good men have been willing to answer questions. Some may prefer not to be named, and none should be suspected of heterodoxy. I would like to thank Ralph Baierlein in particular. I have also had helpful conversations or email exchanges with John Stachel, Francis Everitt, John L. Hall, Edward Teller and one or two others. In England, I have benefited from many stimulating conversations with Stephen Botcherby.

Mainly, however, I am in Howard Hayden's debt, and so is Petr Beckmann.

------◇------

Table of Contents

ACKNOWLEDGMENTS..III

PREFACE VII

INTRODUCTION BY HOWARD C. HAYDEN XIII

CHAPTER 1. RELATIVELY EASY... 1

CHAPTER 2. THE MAGICIAN... 11

CHAPTER 3. MICHELSON-MORLEY.. 19

CHAPTER 4. LORENTZ AND POINCARÉ 31

CHAPTER 5. THE SPECIAL THEORY OF RELATIVITY 37

CHAPTER 6. HOLTON'S CRUSADE 51

CHAPTER 7. ON WHAT EVIDENCE? 59

CHAPTER 8. MYSTERY OF MASS 67

CHAPTER 9. $E = MC^2$ 77

CHAPTER 10. STELLAR ABERRATION 87

CHAPTER 11. SPECTROSCOPIC BINARIES................................... 95

CHAPTER 12. ON BECKMANN'S THEORY 103

CHAPTER 13. THE SAGNAC EXPERIMENT.................................. 109

CHAPTER 14. THE MICHELSON-GALE EXPERIMENT 117

CHAPTER 15. MESONS, MUONS AND TIME DILATION 125

CHAPTER 16. HAFELE AND KEATING 133

CHAPTER 17. GLOBAL POSITIONING SYSTEM 143

CHAPTER 18. THE GENERAL THEORY 153

CHAPTER 19. BENDING OF LIGHT RAYS.................................... 161

CHAPTER 20. MERCURY'S ORBIT.. 171

CHAPTER 21. EINSTEIN'S NEW ETHER...................................... 179

CHAPTER 22. BRILLET AND HALL 185

CHAPTER 23. A HISTORICAL PARALLEL.................................. 191

CHAPTER 24. SYNOPSIS 197

INDEX 201

THE AUTHOR 207

VALES LAKE PUBLISHING.. 209

Preface

The argument of this book is that the experimental consequences of relativity theory can also be reached without relativity. The equation $E = mc^2$ was deduced from relativity theory, but it could also be reached without it and it was so derived as early as 1908. Einstein himself later arrived at the equation without relativity, and he called it his "elementary derivation."

Readers should be warned that this book is the work of a journalist. I have been helped by professional physicists but of course that does not exclude the possibility, even the likelihood, that it contains errors. A non-specialist has more freedom, however, and is less constrained by peer review.

My first guide was Petr Beckmann, a good friend who taught electrical engineering at the University of Colorado for twenty years. It was he who proposed the alternative to Einstein and the thesis of this book. He also made that case in a book published in 1987, *Einstein Plus Two*.

Petr Beckmann's incorruptible skepticism was an inspiration to me. Born in Prague in 1924, he received his Ph.D. in Electrical Engineering from Prague Technical University, then a Doctorate of Science from the Czechoslovak Academy of Sciences. He defected to the United States in 1963, taught at the University of Colorado, and died in Boulder in 1993. He published 60 scientific papers, mostly on electromagnetics and probability theory. His popular book *The History of Pi* reached many readers. His more technical works included *The Scattering of Electromagnetic Waves from Rough Surfaces* (1963), the *Depolarization of Electromagnetic Waves*, and *The Structure of Language* (1973).

He took early retirement in 1981 so that he could concentrate on the book about relativity that he had long planned to write.

Almost as soon as he encountered the special theory of relativity he considered it unsatisfactory, and that conviction never left him. In *Einstein Plus Two* he outlined a theory that is simpler than

Einstein's, and (he argued) consistent with the experimental facts. It dispenses with relativity. At the same time, it accounts for two additional phenomena, ranging from electrons to planets. They are the separation of electron orbits and the Titius-Bode series, which describes planetary distances from the sun, or lunar distances from planets. "No satisfactory explanation of the law has ever been given," Beckmann wrote.

I was privileged to have dozens of conversations and interviews with Petr. He talked about relativity, and he told me the story of his life. He described the high school he had attended in Birmingham, England. Along with other Jewish refugees from Nazi-controlled Czechoslovakia, he had been among the "kinder-transport" of young people sent to England at the beginning of World War II. He told me of his return to a post-war Czechoslovakia, by then Communist, as were his parents. While Petr was lecturing in Colorado in 1963, his father died and he decided to stay in the United States.

When Petr talked about relativity, the difficulties that I had already encountered in "Easy Einstein" books began to melt away. Explanation replaced description, and the natural world, as I saw it, was flooded with light. But his book could not easily convey that, for it was mostly written in the technical language of mathematical physics.

Readers of his newsletter *Access to Energy* will know that Beckmann was a talented and entertaining writer. He could have written a popular account himself, and he considered doing so. But he believed that his ideas had a better chance of being accepted if expressed in technical language. In that he was disappointed. His book was neither criticized not refuted. Most physicists probably never even heard about it.

By the time he died, I had interviewed him extensively, but I also imagined that he would be there to review anything that I wrote. Under his guidance I had written a few articles on relativity for "lay" readers, but I hadn't begun work on the book. Earlier, however, Beckmann had asked several figures in the academy to review the manuscript of *Einstein Plus Two*. One was Howard Hayden, a professor of physics at the University of Connecticut.

At first Hayden supposed that it would be only too easy to find errors. A bold challenge to the orthodoxy, Beckmann's book was hardly believable in places. Special relativity was only tenuously confirmed by the facts, he said. When Hayden read that Einstein's claim about the constancy of the speed of light has *not* been unambiguously shown to be true, he hunted for the experiments that surely would prove Beckmann wrong.

They turned out to be elusive. After much searching, Hayden concluded that they didn't exist. He, too, became convinced that the special theory of relativity, contrary to the way it is portrayed, is based on shaky foundations. He made further discoveries of his own, and in the early 1990s, he gave talks about these ideas to the physics departments of universities in New England. No one even tried to refute what Hayden said.

One of Beckmann's challenges came with a monetary reward, and its details are worth describing. Hayden and Beckmann offered two thousand dollars to the first person who could show where (in the scientific literature) it had been demonstrated that the speed of light is the same east to west as it is west to east. Robert Pool, a journalist at *Science*, heard of the offer, and published it in *Science* magazine. That was in 1990 (vol. 250, page 1208, for those who want to look it up). It was worded as follows:

> Petr Beckmann, professor emeritus of electrical engineering at the University of Colorado, and Howard Hayden, a physicist at the University of Connecticut, will pay $2000 to the first person who offers a valid optical experiment proving that the speed of light on Earth is the same east-to-west as it is west-to-east, within 50 meters per second. The winner doesn't even have to have done the experiment personally.

There were no takers. A reporter with the *Los Angeles Times*, Paul Ciotti, contacted the University of Washington's Clifford Will, an acknowledged expert on relativity, and mentioned the offer. Will's *Was Einstein Right?* had been published a few years earlier. The offer had a deadline, however. The experiment had to have been published before a certain date. Will responded that without this restriction, there were experiments that would qualify for the reward. Hayden then updated the offer and mailed it, "Special Offer to Clifford Will." He received no reply.

It was a key test for Beckmann, because according to his own theory, the speed of light is *not* the same east to west as it is west to east. There should be a small difference, a function of the earth's daily rotation.

A recent comment by the famous physicist Stephen Hawking supports this claim. In *The Universe in a Nutshell* Hawking describes a famous experiment in which two very accurate clocks were flown in opposite directions around the world. "When they met up again the clock that flew toward the east had recorded slightly less time," Hawking wrote. "This might suggest that if one wanted to live longer, one should keep flying to the east so that the plane's speed is added to the earth's rotation."[1]

He was being facetious, of course, but asymmetric time-keeping between east-bound and west-bound clocks has been observed and Einstein had not predicted it. Chapter 16 describes the experiment that Hawking mentions.

By 1990, Petr Beckmann had founded a new physics journal, and he sought contributions from outside the mainstream. Its title was a deliberate oxymoron, although one that would be obscure to most of us: *Galilean Electrodynamics*. After Beckmann's death, Hayden continued as its editor. He has since retired from the University of Connecticut and lives in Colorado, where he teaches part-time at a local college. *Galilean Electrodynamics* has more recently been edited by Cynthia Kolb Whitney, an adjunct professor of physics at Tufts.

Since Petr's death I have acquired a nodding acquaintance with the world of anti-relativity physics. The encounter has not been encouraging. Those who disagree with Einstein often disagree with one another. No single theory is unanimously accepted. One can sympathize with established physicists who pay little attention. Wading through alternatives in search of the errors they probably contain is a task not to be undertaken lightly. Ignoring the whole sideshow is a time-saving strategy.

For these reasons, arguments against special relativity are not likely to persuade those who teach relativity for a living. As Howard Hayden says, if you mention alternative theories, physicists always respond: "Relativity works. And I am going to stick with it as long as it works."[2]

Most observations do seem to conform to the predictions of relativity. I shall also come to anomalies. Hayden's paper on binary stars, published at about the time that Petr Beckmann died, is of particular importance. On his deathbed Beckmann regarded it as a clear falsification of special relativity.[3]

The underlying physical reality that the theory asks us to accept is nonetheless strange. It has always seemed so, and now that a hundred years have passed since its publication, that is unlikely to change. But relativity will not be overthrown by the criticism that it seems paradoxical, or that it defies "common sense." It certainly does, but physicists have little difficulty in brushing such complaints aside.

Change, if it is to come, will have to come from within the physics establishment, and probably as a result of accumulating discrepancies between theory and observation. If so, a consensus could develop around some alternative that resolves the difficulties, making the life of theory easier for all. Beckmann's theory is a candidate, although one cannot discount the possibility that a fatal flaw will be detected within it.

Such an upheaval will probably have to be preceded by a period of subterranean discontent within the physics profession. There are few signs of that. But storms sometimes blow up quickly, and it was interesting to read in a *New York Times* article not long ago that "in science no truth is forever, not even perhaps Einstein's theory of relativity, the pillar of modernity that gave us $E = mc^2$."[4]

Notes to Preface

[1] Stephen Hawking, *The Universe in a Nutshell*, Bantam Press, 2001, p. 9.
[2] All quotations from Howard Hayden are taken from the many conversations I have had with him, unless more specifically noted.
[3] Howard Hayden, "Stellar Aberration," *Galilean Electrodynamics*, v. 4 no. 5, Sept/Oct 1993, p. 92.
[4] Dennis Overbye, "*E* and mc^2: Equality, It Seems, Is Relative," *New York Times*, December 31, 2002.

Petr Beckmann (1924-1993)

Introduction by Howard C. Hayden

Hayden is an emeritus member of the Physics Department at the University of Connecticut, Storrs. He taught there from 1968 to 1999

I first became acquainted with Petr Beckmann when I read his *History of Pi*, a terrific book. I also read his *Health Hazards of NOT Going Nuclear* and subscribed to his newsletter, *Access to Energy*. I had long been interested in energy issues, and it was through our numerous exchanges that we got to know one another. Then, one day, he asked if I would read a book he was writing about something else—relativity theory. He wanted me, as a physicist of essentially standard education and training, to probe the book for errors. Einstein had postulated in his special theory that the speed of light is a constant, and almost everyone in physics believes that. But Beckmann disputed it. He was challenging a basic tenet of relativity, in other words.

I could see from his books that he had his head on straight, but I also knew that he was an electrical engineer, so maybe he hadn't taken the standard physics courses. But he was inclined to trust experiment over theory, which was a good sign, and he was certainly intelligent enough to understand the experiments. So I agreed. If I could stop him from embarrassing himself, I would be doing him a kindness. All too often, people with a brief against Einstein are only acquainted with papers written before about 1920. I had in mind that I would easily be able to find the data that he might have missed.

When I got hold of the book I realized that he understood these experiments perfectly well. An initial reading suggested that, although he might be proved wrong in the details, he was raising issues that were both fundamental and that I had never encountered before.

Let me go over the background. In the 1880s Albert Michelson thought of a way to detect the Earth's motion through the "ether." The ether was to light what the air is to sound—the medium that vibrates as waves pass through it. In its orbital motion around the Sun, the Earth moved through this ether, it was assumed, and

Michelson knew how to make this motion visible with light rays. The instrument he perfected was called an interferometer. Similar devices are used today. They produce a set of parallel, light-and-dark interference lines. If the Earth moves through the ether, as everyone believed, the vertical lines should shift right or left by a measurable amount when the table is rotated.

Michelson tested this in 1887 in his experiment with Edward Morley. But no fringe shift could be seen. The world of physics was thrown into confusion. Then Einstein resolved it with his 1905 paper introducing special relativity. He proposed that the speed of light is constant in all directions, and if that were so, there would be no fringe shift. In the same paper he also decided that the ether itself was "superfluous."

In his book Beckmann restored the ether that Einstein had discarded, but with a new interpretation. In the old view, the ether had been construed as one vast, rarefied substance that filled all of space uniformly. In Beckmann's theory, it was simply the dominant gravitational field. On the Earth, obviously, the dominant field is that of the Earth itself. It merges with the Sun's field somewhere beyond the orbit of the moon, and then the field of the Sun becomes dominant. And so on.

That would immediately explain why Michelson had been unable to detect any motion through the ether. Our gravitational field always accompanies us, as a runner's shadow accompanies the runner. Beckmann's theory can be classified as an "entrained ether" theory. In its orbital motion, the Earth carries its "ether" along with it. But Beckmann also argued that the Earth's gravitational field does *not* swing around with the Earth in its daily rotation. If so, the Earth constantly rotates "through" its gravitational field.

Imagine a woman with a circular waist wearing a hoop skirt. She is the "earth" and her skirt is the "field." As she walks forward, she pirouettes. But, if we eliminate friction as much as possible, her skirt does not rotate with her. So there is a "relative velocity" between her waist and her skirt; likewise between the Earth and its gravitational field. Remember, the gravitational field is the medium in which electromagnetic (including light) waves travel. That is Petr Beckmann's theory in a nutshell.

The Earth's rotational velocity, in the latitudes where these experiments were carried out, is roughly one hundredth of its orbital velocity. For reasons that need not detain us, that fraction has to be squared in calculating the observable effect in Michelson's interferometer. So what Beckmann was saying was that the "fringe-shift" that should have appeared in Michelson's interferometer was real, but ten thousand times smaller than anticipated. Michelson had been looking for an effect caused by the Earth's *orbital* motion. But if Beckmann was right, a much smaller fringe shift caused by the Earth's *rotational* velocity should be present.

I had never seen this raised as an issue. And it implies something else. If the local gravitational field is indeed the luminiferous medium, the speed of light must be different to the east and to the west. Observers on the Earth would measure a higher speed of light coming from the east than from the west. The rotational velocity of the Earth would have to be either added to or subtracted from the speed of light.

Now, the constancy of the speed of light was one of Einstein's most famous claims. It is one of the things that people know about Einstein. And that was where Beckmann's conflict with Einstein would most obviously arise. So I went to the textbooks and looked up references to all those super high-resolution experiments that would prove the speed of light is *not* affected by its direction. I would explain it all to Petr and he would accept it and everything would be okay.

The first problem was that *no* experiments that I could find looked to see if there was any difference between the speed of light to the east and to the west. It would not have been easy to detect anyway. A sensitivity ten thousand times greater than Michelson anticipated could not possibly have been observed with his 1887 equipment. Even today it is not easy.

Eventually, I found the experiment that was said to have the highest sensitivity. That was the Brillet-Hall experiment, published in 1979. It took me some time to get through the jargon and to understand what they had done, but the experiment did have enough sensitivity. What is more, Brillet and Hall did show the effect. It was concealed, although unintentionally, by the way they had presented their data. But it was there. Their results showed the unmistakable signature of the rotation of the Earth. It could be construed as a difference in the speed of light, to the east and west. So I began to think that Petr had a point.

There were other experiments. The first was done in 1913 by Georges Sagnac. He sent light rays clockwise and counterclockwise around a table-top, from one mirror to the next, and back to the starting point. When he rotated the apparatus, he found the fringe-shift that Michelson had looked for. This was demonstrated even before Einstein had published his general theory of relativity.

There followed another milestone. In 1924, Michelson and Henry Gale sent light in both directions around a large rectangle, with an east-west length of over 2000 feet. It showed a fringe shift, attributable to the rotation of the Earth. But the Einsteinians now took the position that the experiment did not qualify as a valid test of special relativity. Nor did the Sagnac experiment. They had found an escape route, which I shall discuss later.

Petr Beckmann called Michelson-Gale "surely the most grandiose interference experiment ever performed." I found that it is barely known, even among physicists. In my entire career I have met no more than half a dozen physicists who have heard of it. Misner, Thorne and Wheeler's big book *Gravitation* has some 1600 references, but Michelson-Gale is not among them, even though Michelson admitted that the experiment is consistent with general relativity. It is not mentioned in the most recent papers that I have seen, claiming to measure the speed of light in various directions.

Two more experiments demonstrated the different speed of light, east and west. In 1971, Hafele and Keating transported atomic clocks around the world on commercial airliners. They found a directional difference in the clock rates. In 1985, the same asymmetry was confirmed on a global scale by Allan, Weiss and Ashby. They bounced electromagnetic signals off orbiting satellites, and found that it takes about 300 nanoseconds longer for the signal to go around the world eastward than westward.

Intrigued by the consistency of these results, I wrote a paper asking: "Is the speed of light isotropic in the laboratory reference frame?" *Isotropic* simply means the same in all directions. To me, that sounded like a good scientific question, even if an east-west difference was not something that Einstein expected. I cited the results from every speed-of-light paper that I could find. But I had a hard time getting it published. I tried *Physical Review*, *Physical Review Letters*, and *The American Journal of Physics*. Neither editors nor reviewers considered the east-west question one that was worth asking. Eventually it was published by *Physics Essays*, a journal that accepts dissident contributions.

At about that time, Petr Beckmann and I offered a reward of $2000 to the first person who could refer us to an experiment demonstrating that the speed of light is the same, east and west, to within 50 meters per second. All we wanted was the reference: journal and page number. A reporter at *Science* magazine published the offer, so it became widely known. But no one took us up on it. Two thousand dollars may not be much, but it's a nice pile of change for a graduate student.

Finally, I discovered an earlier experiment using the extremely sensitive Mössbauer effect. It not only had the sensitivity to detect an east-west differential, but claimed that the speed of light was isotropic to within about two meters per second. But there had been a mistake. The theorist later published an *erratum* saying he had neglected to take "time dilation" into account. In the end, the experiment showed that the speed of light is *not* the same in all directions.

I began to think that Petr might be right, but he warned me that I could be scorned by colleagues. My department at the University of Connecticut probably did regard me as if I were on a wild goose chase. But they knew that I was not idle and that I had done extensive reading of the literature. They did not make me feel uncomfortable in the least. In fact I gave a couple of departmental colloquia on the subject.

I also held colloquia with the physics faculties of about half a dozen universities, mostly in New England. The reception was mainly polite, but skeptical. The slides that raised the most incredulity were photographs of the abstract and the graph of the Hafele-Keating experiment, published in *Science*. The abstract said that for the westbound clocks there was a relativistic time *gain*, and the graph showed how they deduced that from their data.

Textbooks often mention the experiment, but I have never found one that told what actually happened. What happened was a big surprise. When I presented the facts, it was enough of a surprise that some physicists in the audience suspected I was guilty of misrepresentation. At one Canadian university that shall remain nameless one individual made a parting shot as he stomped out: "You come in and show us all this stuff, but how do we know it hasn't been refuted by now?" By and large, however, physicists may have shaken their heads but they weren't hostile. Curiously, however, no one has been able to raise a substantive criticism.

I have added my own little bits and pieces, experimentally. Probably the most interesting was a variation of the Trouton-Noble experiment, done in 1903. Like Michelson-Morley the experiment had a null result, and had seemed to provide strong support for relativity theory. So I redid it, with about 100,000 times more sensitivity. Yet the effect was still "null." But I also showed that the experiment was meaningless. Every theory in town (including Beckmann's) predicted the same outcome. So nothing was being tested. This time, an "orthodox" journal did publish my paper.

Another thing I did was to derive the formula for the bending of starlight—using classical physics. Einstein's most celebrated moment came when he predicted that starlight would bend slightly when passing the Sun. Photographs during a solar eclipse confirmed that, but you don't need relativity to get there. Using a more elementary derivation, I showed that a gravitational field has an index of refraction, and that determines by how much a ray of light will be bent.

The idea here is quite simple. In Beckmann's theory, the luminiferous medium (the gravitational field) is non-uniform. It thins out with distance from the celestial body, whether it be the Sun or the Earth. Light rays do bend by refraction when they move from one medium to another, or move into a medium of different optical density. A pencil in a glass of water appears broken at the surface. My paper on this topic was published in a new journal that Beckmann had founded, *Galilean Electrodynamics*.

Almost immediately, two physicists from China, Tian and Li, independently derived the same formula by another method, again without relativity. One equation they used was identical to mine for the varying speed of light in a gravitational field, but derived by a different method. They used the conservation of energy and of angular momentum to get the same deflection. I'm glad they did it independently, and that their paper was published by *The American Journal of Physics*.

So we have Sagnac's table-top experiment. We have the large-scale experiment by Michelson and Gale. We have Hafele and Keating with their flying clocks. And we have the around-the-world Sagnac experiment, with satellites in Earth orbit. All gave the same result. The best interpretation is that the speed of light for someone on the rotating Earth is $c - v$ to the east, where v is the rotational velocity of the Earth, and $c + v$ to the west. That is the simplest explanation. The speed of light is not a constant, but must have the rotational velocity of the Earth added to or subtracted from it.

Einstein's relativity theory begins with two simple—if counter-intuitive—postulates. Here are some consequences. If A and B are moving uniformly in relation to one another, A thinks that B's meter stick is shorter than his own, and B thinks that A's meter stick is shorter than his own. A thinks that B's clocks tick more slowly than his own, and B thinks that A's clocks tick more slowly than his own. Many words have been needed to reassure students that this is required as a result of Einstein's postulates.

Particles called muons moving at high speed through the atmosphere, or through the vacuum of an accelerator, have longer half-lives than their counterparts at rest in the laboratory. To me, there is nothing odd about that. The bizarre part is that a hypothetical scientist traveling with those high-speed muons would conclude that the muons outside the accelerator have longer half-lives than the ones traveling with him as he speeds along. This latter result has never been tested, and neither has the equally bizarre notion of mutual length contraction.

Relativity theory also predicts dynamical results—things pertaining to mass, momentum, and energy. The most famous is $E = mc^2$. Suffice it to say that these results are the bread and butter not only of the nuclear power industry, but of research accelerators. But physicists should not be too sanguine about how well they support relativity theory. The well-tested equations can be derived without relativity, suggesting that it is not necessary.

So has Einstein been proven wrong? Is Beckmann's theory right? I do think that Einstein's theory will have to be modified for various reasons. But that would require a few lessons in electromagnetics— a sermon for another day. Asymmetry in the speed of light does not in itself contradict special relativity, however. The reason is this. Special relativity theory claims only that the speed of light is constant in an *inertial reference frame*. No acceleration is allowed! Anything that is moving *not* in a straight line is non-inertial. And the rotating Earth is non-inertial by definition, because centrifugal forces and curvilinear paths are always present. In practice, however, Einsteinians use this escape route only with experimental results that don't fit the special theory.

The Michelson-Morley experiment, for example, looked for a fringe-shift predicted by classical physics. They did not find it, and that made it consistent with special relativity. But if a more accurate Michelson-Morley experiment were to find a fringe shift the Einsteinians would probably conclude that special relativity does not apply in that instance. On the surface of the rotating earth, the experiment would be seen as non-inertial.

Petr Beckmann said somewhere that the special theory is close to being inherently irrefutable. The experiments we are talking about have all been done on the surface of the Earth, or nearly so. And anything in that location is moving around in a big circle and subjected to centrifugal forces. Acceleration is present. So the theory has this built-in "catch" that prevents it from being refuted.

The first time the relativists were confronted with an awkward result—the Sagnac experiment—they responded by pointing to its non-inertial features; the same with Michelson-Gale. Perhaps the best we can do is to get them to admit that their theory is unfalsifiable. And remember, protection against refutation is not a strength but a great weakness of any theory.

As for the general theory of relativity—often called a theory of gravity—it may ultimately be shown that it gives the same results as Beckmann's, but by a far more circuitous route.

One test that hasn't been done and could be: a Michelson-Morley experiment on the space shuttle. In low-earth orbit, the shuttle flies at something like seven kilometers per second. This compares to 30 kilometers a second for the Earth's orbital velocity. With the shuttle moving through the gravitational field at this speed, the fringe shift should be easily detected with modern equipment. Anyway, I predict that a fringe shift would show. The relativists would predict that it wouldn't. If it did, I further predict they would then say that the reference frame of the shuttle is non-inertial and therefore special relativity was unscathed. So it goes.

What about Beckmann's theory? I'm not saying it will get off scot-free either. He wrote that he was "not so naïve as to think that the first attempt to move the entire Einstein theory *en bloc* onto classical ground will turn out to be perfectly correct." What he aimed for was "the return of physics from description to comprehension."

Petr's theory, straightforward in outline, is complicated in the zones where gravitational fields overlap. We are obviously "in" the Earth's field, for example, but we are also in the Sun's. As we move away from the Earth, our field gets weaker and soon we come to a place where the "dominant" field switches from that of the Earth to that of the Sun. Beckmann never worked out the mathematics of these intermediate zones. He assumed that they would be complex, but that nothing fundamental about the underlying physics would change. The transitional region is "marked by the properties of most transients: difficult and of secondary importance," he wrote.

I will conclude with a few thoughts on stellar aberration, which could cause trouble for relativity. The facts of stellar aberration, known since 1728, are not in dispute. As the Earth moves in its orbit, the position of a star varies slightly, depending on its direction relative to the Earth's motion. Just as a man running in the rain must incline his umbrella forward if he is to stay dry, so a telescope must be angled forward if the starlight is to enter the telescope. The forward inclination is the angle of aberration. All stars have the same maximum angle of aberration—about 20 seconds of arc.

In his special relativity paper, Einstein used the same method to derive the formulae for the Doppler Effect (which exists for both light and sound), and for stellar aberration. Einstein argued that the aberration of starlight is simply a function of the relative velocity of the star and the Earth. But if the stars in the sky are moving at different speeds relative to us, why do they all show the same aberration? By Einstein's theory there should be different aberrations for different stars. But that isn't so.

In Einstein's day, however, this was a criticism without teeth. No one knew the velocities of the stars, relative to Earth. Today, however, we have evidence from binary star systems, which revolve around each other at close range and at high speeds. At a given point in their mutual orbiting, one star must be moving more or less the same direction we are moving, and the other one in the opposite direction, irrespective of the real motion of the binary system as a whole. By Einstein's theory, then, the two stars of the binary pair should show different aberrations. They should appear to separate, merge, and separate again, optically. Moreover, that angular separation ought to be *huge* compared to the small angle of aberration measured by astronomers. But that doesn't happen. The two binary stars remain as a single unresolvable point in the sky. In fact, we only know they *are* binaries because of the to-and-fro Doppler shifts in their spectral lines.

The criticism was made in a recent book, and I don't see how the relativists escape it. If relative velocity is what matters, there should be visible, alternating separation and closure between the two stars of a binary system. But it is never seen. The method that Einstein used, linking the derivation of aberration and the Doppler Effect, seemed economical at the time but it has the relativists pinned like a knight's fork in chess. If they say that Einstein really meant that some *other* velocity applies to aberration, they end up with the wrong formula for the Doppler Effect.

Well, I have covered a lot of ground. Tom Bethell takes you over much the same terrain, step by step. If you don't understand relativity theory now—and you have lots of company— bear this in mind.   Despite the simplicity of relativity's postulates, the complications mount up in a hurry. By the time you have finished the book you may conclude that relativity is an inessential theory that introduces unnecessary complications into physics. Petr's alternative seems far more satisfactory to me.

Chapter 1. Relatively Easy

Einstein's special theory of relativity was published in 1905; his much more difficult general theory was completed ten years later. A strong consensus of physicists and learned laymen agrees that the special theory has been confirmed over and over again, and by now can hardly be denied. It has been verified in particle accelerators, validated by the Global Positioning System, popularized by the equation $E = mc^2$. Accelerated particles live longer lives, GPS has relativistic corrections built into it, $E = mc^2$ was derived by Einstein using relativity theory. And yes, atom bombs do work.

It follows that anyone who disputes the special theory does so at his peril and probably doesn't understand the experiments that have confirmed it. When it comes to the general theory of relativity, the consensus is less confident. The theory is said to be inconsistent with quantum mechanics, and is still subjected to testing, like a patient who must go in for lab tests. Aspects of the general theory may eventually have to be revised.

These verdicts are more or less reversed in this book. I argue that the special theory is inconsistent with recent (and some not-so-recent) experiments, and that the speed of light is *not* a constant. It is the special theory, not the general theory that seems to need repair; perhaps even to be discarded. The general theory, on the other hand, does seem to give the right results, although by a complicated method. It takes a difficult mountain path when all along an easier route leads us to the same destination.

It was Petr Beckmann who found this easier path, although a recent book, *Einstein and the Ether*, shows that Einstein came close to discovering it himself. Anyway, the general theory may work well enough as long as we don't object to its difficult route. Einstein himself was obliged to take it, lest he risk repudiating his own special theory; the repairs it needed had perforce turned his general theory into a cumbersome thing. For the rest of us, however, the pitfalls of special relativity can be skirted altogether and at that point general relativity not only becomes manageable, but begins to look a whole lot like Petr Beckmann's theory.

That is the argument of this book.

I hope to set these things out in a way that is intelligible to non-specialists. Public interest in relativity has always been high, and works of alleged simplification keep rolling off the presses. I call them Easy Einstein books. Sometimes I think that people just keep looking and looking—and what they are looking for is one that they can understand. People have often told me that they have found such books easy enough for the first few pages, but then, and often abruptly, they find themselves out of their depth. Something doesn't seem to add up. At that point they are inclined to abandon their project, which was to understand relativity.

The truth is that such books are not easy. Not at all. The hardest one I ever saw, *Relativity Demystified*, starts out with the Maxwell equations, assumes we know what "curl" refers to, and goes on to discuss Cartan structure equations, nonholomonic bases and null tetrads. Yet the back cover claims it is "simple enough for beginners."[1] A spoof, maybe?

Yet even in books that do earnestly try to instruct us, it is not the math that is difficult. Special relativity involves nothing worse than high school algebra. But the great majority of us never master the theory. I hope to explain the source of this difficulty.

It's fair to say that the special theory has an easy part and a difficult part. This chapter will deal exclusively with the easy part. Nothing in it will dissent from professional opinion or disturb the conventional interpretation. I shall postpone the difficult part until readers have some idea of what it's all about. Arts majors should have no difficulties at this stage, and physicists no objections.

From the beginning, popular accounts of relativity have located everything on railroads and trains. We encounter workers outside on embankments, and guards inside. The first writer to take this approach was Einstein himself, in his popular account, *Relativity: The Special and the General Theory*. Its cover promises "a clear explanation that anyone can understand"; an earlier edition promised the same for those "with only a high school education." That may have given rise to feelings of inadequacy over the years, for the book is *in part* easily understood, and *in part* quite difficult. The same could be said for just about all the other "Easy Einstein" books.

I shall follow Einstein's lead by locating events on a railroad car, or, as his English translation puts it, railway carriage. As someone who traveled quite a bit in railway carriages in his youth, I shall follow Einstein in that respect, too. By page 16, Einstein is alluding to "our old friend the railway carriage," and his casual tone helps to sustain the hope, even if it proves to be short-lived, that we can expect to be comfortable with what follows.

What is important is to pinpoint the transition, when the explanation ceases to be clear and quickly turns into something that seems illogical or hard to accept. In this chapter I shall proceed up to that dividing line.

On the Train

There's a familiar railway experience that we all have had. It is real enough, not just a thought experiment (of which there are too many in books on relativity). It allows us to encounter relativity at its most basic level. The train is waiting at a station, and you are in a window seat. Next to you is another train, almost close enough to touch. Then you see you have started to glide forward. You hardly felt a thing—but that can happen with trains. When the other train disappears from view, you see with a slight shock the stationary platform beyond. It was the other train that had been moving. You hadn't felt a thing because you had been motionless all along.

If you had been more alert—or looking out of the window on the other side—you could easily have seen that you were stationary. Anyway, the experience illustrates the point that there are situations in which we cannot easily tell whether we are moving or not.

Assume now that it is night, the track is smooth, and the blinds are down. The train is moving in a straight line, at a constant speed. Then again, maybe it is stationary. How would you know? Your task is to conduct some experiment within the train to help you to decide whether the train is moving. The claim of relativity theory is simply that *no physics experiment inside that environment* would give you the answer.

That is the special theory of relativity in a nutshell.

You can throw a ball straight up in the air, and it will land in your lap whether the train is stationary or racing along at a hundred miles an hour. You can try other experiments, recalled from the physics lab. You can roll ball bearings down an inclined plane, heat up water with a Bunsen burner, stir chemicals into an explosive mixture. The results will be unaffected by the motion of the train— just as long as it is uniform, in a straight line.

This also helps us to establish the key distinction between the special and the general theory. In its details (and its mathematics) the general theory is much the more difficult. The special theory deals only with motion that is uniform and non-accelerated. If acceleration is involved we must turn to the general theory.

Right now we shall deal only with the special theory. In the train puzzle that I have described—with the blinds down, how can we tell if the train is moving? —you would know the answer immediately if the train headed into a curve. You would feel yourself leaning over to one side. If the train accelerated, you would feel yourself pushed back into your seat. And if *you* could feel those things, so could scientific instruments.

Therefore, if we want to say that "no experiment" can disclose whether the train is moving or not, we mean non-accelerated motion only. That, obviously, is a special case of motion in general; hence special theory.   Most movement involves bumps, turns, or acceleration. But those kinds of motion do not meet the condition imposed by the special theory.

Einstein disliked this restriction—that relativity applied only to uniform motion. And he knew how difficult it would be to apply it to accelerated as well as to uniform motion. One of his earliest supporters, Max Planck, outright discouraged the attempt. But the "generalization" of that principle to accelerated motion is what Einstein achieved in his general theory.

Happiest Thought

Early on, Einstein concluded that the gravitational force we all experience seems to be indistinguishable from the inertial forces we feel when we are accelerated. It was a great insight, and he referred to it as his "happiest thought." The general theory is often referred to as a theory of gravity, and that is because the effects of acceleration can be made to "stand in" for gravity. Physicists welcome that substitution because acceleration is more amenable to investigation. We can accelerate things deliberately and see what happens. But we can neither intensify nor eliminate the gravitational force as long as we are on the surface of the Earth.

Einstein found that he could make the argument that, even if you are in a train with the blinds down, so that you feel the push or pull of acceleration or centrifugal force, you still can't be *entirely* sure that your vehicle is accelerating. Perhaps, instead, you suddenly entered a different gravitational field? That is unlikely. But who could say it was impossible?

In devising the general theory of relativity, the intellectual challenge confronting Einstein was great and the mathematics complicated. Few people understood it at the time (or since). That is why it took him ten years while at the top of his game. In the end he came up with a theory that impressed almost everyone. The most important reason why scientists were impressed was that the new theory accounted for the few celestial anomalies that Newton's theory of gravitation had been unable to account for.

At its simplest, then, special relativity is the theory that the laws of physics are unaffected by the motion of the laboratory. If so, physics *experiments* cannot reveal such motion either. It has become conventional to state the theory of relativity in this way.

In *Simply Einstein*, Richard Wolfson, a professor of physics at Middlebury College, says: "The theory of relativity is, in its barest essence, just the simple statement that regardless of one's state of motion the laws of physics are the same."[2] He imagines a cruise ship with a tennis court. It steams forward at 30 knots, and the court is enclosed. There is no wind blowing the ball, no waves rocking the boat, no helmsman turning the rudder. Under such conditions the game will proceed exactly as if the ship were in port.

We can easily accept that.

"So you already know and believe the essence of relativity," Wolfson cheerfully continues. "In that sense, you can close this book and be done with it."

Well, no. We can't accept that. Otherwise those Easy Einstein books wouldn't be so confusing! There are still many hurdles to surmount. But it is true that at this point we do know something important about relativity. That is the good news.

The problem is that the understanding of relativity discussed so far was already known to Galileo and Newton. Galileo even located his "relativistic" scenario on a ship. In his *Dialogue Concerning the Two Chief Systems of the World*, published in 1632, he wrote:

> Shut yourself up with some friend in the main cabin below decks on some large ship and have with you there some flies, butterflies, and other small flying animals. Have a large bowl of water with some fish in it; hang up a bottle which empties drop by drop into a wide vessel beneath it. With the ship standing still, observe carefully how

> the little animals fly with equal speed to all sides of the cabin. The
> fish swim indifferently in all directions, the drops fall into the vessel
> beneath; and in throwing something toward your friend, you need
> throw it no more strongly in one direction than another. . . . [Then]
> have the ship proceed with any speed you like, so long as the motion
> is uniform and not fluctuating this way and that. You will discover
> not the least change in all the effects named, nor could you tell from
> any of them whether the ship was moving or standing still.[3]

So said Galileo 377 years ago. The same idea was stated more
formally and briefly by Isaac Newton in Book 1 of his *Principia*
(1687): "The momenta of the bodies included in a given space are
the same, whether that space is at rest or whether it moves uniformly
in a straight line without rotation."

And that, in a sense, is the bad news.

In part, relativity theory is easily understood. Then we find out
that that easy part was well known and ingeniously explained
hundreds of years ago. So the difficulties all lie ahead.

There's another way of expressing the easy part of relativity,
and it was discussed by Alan Lightman on PBS at the time of the
centenary of Einstein's theory.

> Ray Suarez: The theory of relativity is 100 years old this month. But
> I'll bet a lot of people would be hard pressed to say what it is. So, in
> a short, sweet way, what is the theory of relativity?
> Alan Lightman: The fundamental idea of relativity is that there is no
> condition of absolute rest—that any motion is relative to another
> body. If you're traveling at 70 miles per hour, what that means is
> you're going at 70 miles per hour relative to the road.
> But the highway is stuck to the Earth, the Earth is spinning
> around, it's orbiting the Sun at a certain speed, the Sun is moving
> around the center of the galaxy at another speed, the galaxy is
> traveling through space. And you cannot really say how fast your
> car is going in an absolute sense, only how fast is going relative to
> the highway. And that's where the word relativity comes from.[4]

Lightman is making the same basic point. In the enclosed train, we
can't say if we are moving or not because we can't say what (if
anything) we are moving relative to. Lightman's point has also been
put this way: the universe has no hitching post. We can only say
how fast we are moving relative to something else. There is no
absolute motion.

Now we come to an important elaboration, and it will point to what is to come. Things do get a little more difficult here, but we still won't reach the point where common sense rebels.

Electricity and Magnetism

The idea that inside an enclosed laboratory no physics experiment can tell whether it is moving or not, was true of the laws of physics as they were known in Newton's day. By the 19th century, however, physics embraced something new: electromagnetism. Now there were new laws, and many scientists had contributed to them. The most important was James Clerk Maxwell, much admired by Einstein. His framed picture was in his Princeton study.

With electromagnetism, including the propagation of light, it was no longer expected that the old relativity principle would hold true. If your laboratory was in motion then there should be a way of detecting that motion—perhaps in some "absolute" way. There was a simple reason for this. Electromagnetic phenomena travel in waves, so it was assumed they had a medium to wave in. It was given a name: Ether. Often in the 19th century it was spelled aether.

Maxwell said that this ether filled the entirety of space. It was the largest and most uniform body of which we have any knowledge, he wrote.[5] In the mind's eye it is appropriate to think of Maxwell's ether as composed of tiny particles, much smaller than atoms, or perhaps a fluid-like substance, which fills all of space. A ray of light is like a ripple that propagates through this ether, and does so at the enormous speed of 186,000 miles per second.

The evidence for the wave nature of light was so strong that scientists were confident they would soon detect the Earth's passage through this ether. Since the Earth was moving around the Sun, it surely moved *through* this medium. To be sure, the direction and speed of the Earth's passage through it was not known. It was not necessarily the direction of the Earth in its orbit, because, as Lightman reminded us, the Sun has its own separate motion through the galaxy. But that was a detail. The point was that the Earth's passage through the ether could in principle be detected, much as a passenger in a moving car can feel the slipstream by putting his finger out of the window and estimate his speed.

Presumably, then, an experiment could detect and measure the Earth's passage through the ether. If it succeeded, physicists would have found an optical way of detecting motion in the equivalent of an enclosed railroad car with the blinds down. In the 1880s, first in Germany and then the United States, ingenious experiments were set up to detect this "ether wind."

At the same time, if motion through the ether were detected, a divergence would have opened up between the two sets of physical laws. There were the laws of mechanics, associated with Newton and Galileo, for which (all agreed) the "principle of relativity" applied: Uniform motion could only be detected relative to something else. Secondly, there were the laws of electromagnetics, associated with Clerk Maxwell, for which uniform motion through the ether *could* be detected.

Could be, and (it was assumed) soon would be.

If that expectation were met, nature would embody a "double standard." The relativity principle—the idea that in an enclosed space you can't distinguish between uniform motion and stillness— would be true of the laws of mechanics; but *not* true of electromagnetism.

Einstein's special theory can therefore be seen as his pursuit of the idea that there is no double standard in nature; that just as absolute motion cannot be detected in mechanical experiments, so it also could not be detected in electromagnetic experiments.

A desire to impute this underlying consistency to nature was what drove Einstein. In his own popular book, written in 1916, setting forth both the special and the general theories, he more than once returns to this point. "That a principle of such broad generality should hold with such exactness in one domain of phenomena [the laws of mechanics] and yet should be invalid for another [the domain of electromagnetism] is *a priori* not very probable," he wrote.[6]

Pursuit of Simplicity

In searching for an underlying consistency, Einstein was pursuing a goal that Isaac Newton and the classical physicists would have applauded. If there is anything that we admire in Newton's laws of motion, and of gravity, it is their simplicity. In science, truth, beauty and simplicity do mostly seem to go together. Einstein, too, sought a simplifying unity.

So what happened? In 1881, the crucial experiment that was intended to detect the Earth's passage through the ether was carried out by Albert A. Michelson in Potsdam. It was repeated many times, most famously in 1887 by Michelson again, this time with the help of Edward Morley. They were unable to show that our passage through the ether produced any effect at all.

According to the underlying physical theory of the time, the experiment should have produced a visible effect. Einstein's response was to propose a revolutionary restructuring of physics. The same rule that was already accepted with respect to mechanics must now be applied to electromagnetics, he postulated. As long as motion was uniform, there was no way in principle that it could be detected by *any* physical experiment, whether the phenomenon was mechanical or electromagnetic.

Nothing less than "revolutionary" does the new theory justice. "All of physics had to be reformulated after Einstein," Alan Lightman said in his PBS interview, "to incorporate this strange new notion of the relative nature of time—that different clocks in motion relative to each other tick at different rates."

I anticipate that readers will already be waving their arms and saying they don't understand why Lightman said that. And there is no reason why they should. His remarks have already thrown us into the deep end of the relativity pool—into the difficult part that we are going to have to master.

Notice, also, that in attempting to simplify physics by unifying its laws, Einstein seems to have ended up rewriting them and making everything more complicated. And in so doing, did he not defeat his original purpose? Certainly dissenters like Petr Beckmann, who as soon as they learned relativity were inclined to believe that there had to be an easier way, were influenced by this consideration.

So let us proceed at a more leisurely pace. I shall review the Michelson-Morley experiment and its perplexing result, but before doing so I want to take a side excursion and say something preliminary about the "relatively difficult" part of relativity theory.

Its difficulty is of a peculiar kind. If we see a page of Latin, and we know only a little of the language, translating it will be difficult. With a dictionary we may be able to do so. A page of mathematics may present us with comparable difficulties. But special relativity isn't like that. The math is simple—in fact it need not be brought in at all. The difficulty is more like our experience when we watch a magic performance. Something unexpected happens, and our strong inclination is to respond in this fashion:

"Can you go over that again, only this time more slowly?"

In case you suspect that your own intellectual shortcomings are to blame if you don't quite get what Einstein is up to, I shall supply a few testimonials to the contrary, in the next chapter. They will be from experts in the field. Their effect, I hope, will be to persuade you that *everyone* encounters these difficulties. *All* of us are inclined to respond: Can you go over that again, more slowly? So that is what I shall do.

Notes: Chapter 1

[1]   David McMahon, *Relativity Demystified*, McGraw-Hill, 2006.

[2]   Richard Wolfson, *Simply Einstein*, W.W. Norton, 2003, p. 14.

[3]   Galileo Galilei, *Dialogue Concerning the Two Chief World Systems*, University of California Press, 1953, p. 186.

[4]   Interview with Alan Lightman, "PBS News Hour with Jim Lehrer," June 16, 2005.

[5]   James Clerk Maxwell, "Ether," *Encyclopedia Britannica*, 9th ed., 1875 vol. 8, pp. 568-72.

[6]   Albert Einstein, *Relativity, the Special and the General Theory*, 15th ed, 1952, Crown, p. 14.

Chapter 2. The Magician

Here is an impressive testimonial to the difficulty that we shall encounter. It comes from a man who taught physics at Princeton University in the 1950s. His name was Eric Rogers, and he and Einstein were neighbors and friends. He was considered to be such a good teacher—he taught a popular course to non-science students—that he was made a full professor even though he didn't have a graduate degree. He also wrote a beguiling tome called *Physics for the Inquiring Mind*, reprinted many times, and illustrated by himself.

In his book, he offers what he calls "an annoying, untrue fable to warn you of the difficulty of accepting Relativity." It is "distressing to good mathematical physicists," he says, but we shall find that what it "alleges so impossibly does occur in relativistic adding of velocities."

In the fable he asks us to watch a "magic trick." A conjurer takes an empty bag, which we can inspect beforehand. He puts in two balls, then two more. The bag is then found to contain five balls. It's not an illusion, and we can repeat the exercise as often as we like. So what do we conclude? *"In some cases*, 2 + 2 do not make 4," Rogers says. "The rules of mathematics must be modified." We are not faced with this paradox in real life, he allows. But with "motion through space," we really are.[1]

That from a professor who taught at Princeton. It is helpful for beginners because it allows us to believe that our puzzlement, which surely will arise, may well have nothing to do with our own shortcomings. After all, we know perfectly well that 2 + 2 make four. Apparently there is something strange that we shall have to come to grips with.

One day Rogers met Einstein coming out of his house at Princeton. Rogers told him that he was scheduled for an operation. Rogers then imitated Einstein's German accent:

"Don't worry," Einstein said. "Zose doctors are vizards!"[2]

No, it was Einstein who was the wizard. *In some cases*, he could show that two and two don't make four.

This is not the last time that we shall find Einstein compared to a wizard or a magician. One of his biographers, Banesh Hoffmann, who worked with Einstein in the 1930s, made the same comparison. We shall come to his illuminating account of Einstein's stage-magic in chapter 5.

Here is a more recent statement of the difficulty that Rogers tells us about.   Corey S. Powell, a senior editor at *Discover* magazine, says in *God in the Equation* that, despite hundreds of attempts to "translate" relativity for the lay public, "the theory remains stubbornly counterintuitive." He gives this illustration:

If a train is moving forward at 10 miles per hour, and a passenger runs down the corridor in the same direction, also at 10 miles per hour, "Einstein argued that he is actually traveling a bit less than 20 miles per hour."[3] Relative to the ground, that is. He sounds like Rogers, but what he says is literally true in Einstein's theory.

For a change of pace, here is a testimonial from David Mermin, who taught "sophisticated" high school teachers who met at Cornell University in the summer.   The course was intended "to make them believe that special relativity was not inconsistent or paradoxical." His book *Space and Time in Special Relativity*, based on these lectures, includes the following passage. I am in full agreement with what he says, *except for* the five-word phrase that I have italicized near the end.

The special theory of relativity, alone among the areas of modern physics, can in large part be honestly explained to someone with no formal background in physics and none in mathematics beyond a little algebra and geometry.   This is quite remarkable.   One can popularize the quantum theory at the price of gross oversimplification and distortion, ending up with a rather uneasy compromise between what the facts dictate and what is possible to convey in ordinary language.   In relativity, on the contrary, a straightforward and rigorous development of the subject can be completely simple.

Nevertheless, special relativity is one of the hardest subjects for a beginner to grasp, for its very simplicity emphasizes the distressing fact that its basic notions are in direct contradiction to certain simple, commonplace notions that almost everyone fully grasps and believes, *even though they are wrong.* As a result teaching relativity is rather like conducting psychotherapy.   It is not enough simply to state what is going on, for there is an enormous amount of resistance to be broken down.[4]

One of those commonplace notions (but wrong, according to Einstein) that we do fully grasp and believe is that a man running at 10 mph within a train that is moving at 10 mph in the same direction will be moving (relative to the ground) at 20 mph.

Obviously, we shall have to learn why Einstein says that is wrong. And having learned that lesson, we will be well on our way to understanding the special theory of relativity.

Sometimes even graduate students have a hard time with special relativity, as recent articles in the *American Journal of Physics* claimed.

Over a period of five years, the Physics Education Group at the University of Washington investigated the understanding of "key ideas" in relativity, including that of a reference frame. Even after instruction, the group found, "two thirds of physics undergraduates and one third of graduate students are unable to apply the construct of a reference frame in determining whether or not two events are simultaneous." ("Reference frame" I shall come to.)

The Central Difficulty

Those doing the survey found that it was the most "basic, underlying concepts" that students find difficult. They found also that for most students, "the implications of special relativity are in strong conflict with their intuitions."[5]

This is perfectly understandable, and the problem, I believe, is that the special theory of relativity itself undermines our intuitions about basic underlying concepts—the most basic of which are space and time. In fact, it could be said that teaching special relativity and teaching the "basic underlying concepts" of physics are in pedagogical conflict.

Many technical terms can be translated into something simpler, but "reference frame" is one that will keep coming up. There is nothing difficult about it other than a lack of familiarity. Essentially, a reference frame is a block of space. A simple example, as we have seen, is a railroad car. Something whose parts are rigidly connected is said to constitute a reference frame. An automobile is another. So is a second automobile that is overtaking the first. A train moving down the track is one reference frame, the track itself is another; a train going in the opposite direction is a third, and so on.

The number of possible reference frames is infinite. But if such a frame is moving in a straight line at a constant speed, it is said to be an "inertial frame," and the rules of special relativity apply. Sometimes you see the phrase "coordinate system" instead of reference frame; Einstein used it, and it means the same thing. A reference frame can be of any size.

The crucial point is that all its parts move rigidly together, if they move at all. There is no relative motion between its parts. A train with lots of cars linked together by flexible couplings, so that it can take a curve without falling off the rails, would *not* be an inertial reference frame—while it was on the curve. I don't think physicists would want to think of it as any kind of a reference frame because all the angular stresses and forces would give them too many headaches.

Copernicus Revisited?

A few words from the philosopher Bertrand Russell, whose book *The ABC of Relativity* was published in 1925. He anticipates on his very first page the psychological difficulty that I have mentioned. Of the popular accounts of relativity, he wrote (a few had already begun to appear) they "generally cease to be intelligible just at the point where they begin to say something important." He exonerated the popularizers, who had done their best. Furthermore, he said, the ideas of relativity can be expressed without mathematics, but are "none the less difficult on that account."

To overcome our difficulty, he wrote, we must "change our imaginative picture of the world." This he elaborated upon, concluding with a prediction that has not been borne out in the 80-odd years since his book was published.

> The same sort of change was demanded by Copernicus, when he taught that the earth is not stationary and the heavens do not revolve about it once a day. To us now there is no difficulty in this idea, because we learned it before our mental habits became fixed. Einstein's ideas, similarly, will seem easy to a generation which has grown up with them; but for our generation a certain effort of imaginative reconstruction is unavoidable.[7]

This analogy is often made by Einstein's popularizers, but I believe it is doubly in error. In the first place, the heliocentric system never was particularly difficult to grasp. Astronomers in ancient Greece accepted it. As to relativity, three or four generations have passed, and the difficulty that Bertrand Russell saw —comparable to accepting that simple addition no longer yields the familiar results— shows no sign of going away.

In fact, the same difficulty was restated in an article about Einstein in *Natural History* magazine, published in 2003.

"We live in Einstein's universe," Richard Panek wrote. Nonetheless, special relativity, with its high school algebra, "still does manage to defy the imagination. Try as we might, we find we find it very difficult to get our minds around it."

He, too, compares our mystification to that allegedly experienced at the time of Copernicus. "And as we learn to change the way we think about the world, the nuances of relativity, too, can start to make as much sense as that the Earth goes around the sun."[7]

Actually, it is not the "nuances" of relativity that cause problems, but the fundamentals, as we just saw with the student surveys. The truth is that "the way we think about the world" not only has *not* changed in basic ways, but the difficulty embedded within relativity has emerged more plainly into view in the last century.

Special and General Theories

Although special relativity is simple in its mathematics, as these things go, while general relativity is abstruse, the conceptual difficulty may actually be greater with the former. For all its complexities, there are aspects of general relativity that we can get our minds around. Most of us have seen those pictures of a heavy ball, representing the Sun, sitting on a sheet of stretched rubber. It distorts the sheet, so that a ball bearing rolled in from the periphery is forced into a circular path around the "Sun."

The idea is that the stretched sheet is analogous to the gravitational field of the Sun. Its mass, we are told, distorts "space-time" near the Sun.

"Space-time" is not something we can easily grasp. Still, we get the idea that a distortion of space near the ball makes the ball-bearing behave *as though* a force emanates from the center. A distortion in space produces the same effect as a force—the force of gravity. And so we think we are at least on the way to understanding something about general relativity. Maybe we will never understand the mathematics. But that doesn't matter. There's a "big picture" that we partly do get. We don't feel that it defies logic.

Many of us do feel that way, however, when we encounter the special theory for the first time. If the difficulty lay only in the math, high-school graduates would have no problems with the special theory. Yet physics graduate students, people with advanced degrees, eminent philosophers and learned laymen encounter this difficulty.

As I said earlier, special relativity is regarded as true, proved, confirmed, and repeatedly demonstrated. But general relativity still evokes questions. For over 40 years, and at a cost estimated at $750 million, Stanford University prepared an experiment—Gravity Probe B, it was called—to test in space a prediction of the general theory. Finally launched in 2004, it is now orbiting the Earth on a satellite. Implicit in this experiment, of course, is the possibility that the general theory could be shown to be false.

C. W. Francis Everitt, the director of Gravity Probe B, spent most of his professional career working on the Probe B experiment. He also wrote a hard-to-find book about Clerk Maxwell. In response to my query about the status of the two theories of relativity, he replied:

> Let me give you my own general feeling. I would not be at all surprised if Einstein's general theory of relativity were to break down. Einstein himself recognized some serious shortcomings in it, and we know on general grounds that it is very difficult to reconcile with other parts of modern physics. With regard to special relativity, on the other hand, I would be much more surprised. The experimental foundations do seem to be much more compelling.
>
> Needless to say, intuitions such as this can be wrong, and if indeed an experimentalist felt inclined to perform the test you mention, one would encourage it. One does, however, have to make choices (right or wrong) about what oneself is going to do and my own prejudice has made me concentrate on tests of the general theory.[8]

(I had mentioned the possibility of repeating the Michelson-Morley experiment—the topic of the next chapter—but looking for an effect very much smaller than the one that Michelson had expected to see. The proposed new experiment is central to the alternative thesis advanced in this book.)

A comparable assessment of the two theories of relativity was made by the late Edward Teller when I interviewed him in 1993. "General relativity can be questioned," he said. "Special relativity is as firmly established as Euclid's geometry."

The occasion was a conference in Oakland honoring Petr Beckmann, who had recently died. Teller had known Beckmann well and told me that he loved to read *Access to Energy*, Beckmann's newsletter. But he disagreed with him about special relativity. I made detailed notes as I interviewed Teller and wrote up a memorandum immediately. Here is a paragraph from that memo:

> The essence of general relativity is that space is curved, Teller said. You can imagine a two dimensional thing being curved (into a third), but it is impossible to imagine three-dimensional space as curved. How much harder, then, to imagine four-dimensional space-time as curved. But general relativity says that this four-dimensional thing, which you cannot imagine, is curved. Einstein came up with the mathematics of this unimaginable thing. Teller is not entirely comfortable with the idea.[9]

Most physicists in this field would agree with Teller and Everitt about the relative strengths of special and general relativity. It is often said that the two "pillars" of modern physics, quantum theory and general relativity, don't fit together properly. One or the other may have to be modified.

In any event, a physicist who expresses nuanced doubts about general relativity, or offers refinements to it, will get a hearing from his colleagues— or those who can assess what he is saying. On the other hand, a physicist who entertains doubts about the special theory might well keep them to himself. For as the textbooks tell us, it has been tested, confirmed and repeatedly shown to be true.

I don't think that is right. It is the special theory that will need closer scrutiny. But, first, a closer look at the most important experiment that led up to it: the Michelson-Morley experiment.

Notes Chapter 2

[1]   Eric M. Rogers, *Physics for the Inquiring Mind,* Princeton, 1960, pp. 480-81.

[2]   Author's interview with Ralph Baierlein, April, 2004.   He heard the story from Rogers.

[3]   Corey S. Powell, *God in the Equation*, Free Press, N.Y. 2002, p. 57.

[4]   N. David Mermin, *Space and Time in Special Relativity*, McGraw Hill. N.Y. 1968, p vii.

[5]   "Student understanding of time in special relativity: simultaneity and reference frames," *Am.   J. Physics*, July 2001, pp. S24-S35.   "The challenge of changing deeply held beliefs about the relativity of simultaneity," *Am. J. Physics*, December 2002, pp. 1238-1248.

[6]   Bertrand Russell, *ABC of Relativity*, Harper & Brothers, N.Y. 1925, pp. 1-2.

[7]   Richard Panek, "And Then There Was Light," *Natural History*, November 2002.

[8]   Letter to author from Francis Everitt, January 13, 1994.

[9]   Author's interview with Edward Teller, August 14, 1993; Teller's banquet remarks were reprinted in a special edition of *Access to Energy*, v. 21, Oct. 1993.

Chapter 3. Michelson-Morley

Until the mid-1960s, most books on relativity referred the origin of Einstein's theory to the Michelson-Morley experiment, and the great perplexity that it had provoked. Largely due to the revisionist campaign of Gerald Holton of Harvard, however, that interpretation fell out of favor.[1] But I believe the older way was correct, and I shall revert to it here. Einstein's theory is also much easier to understand if it is considered in the light of Michelson-Morley. Later, I shall discuss "Holton's Crusade."

In other respects, however, this chapter accepts the conventional interpretation of Michelson-Morley. The experiment was expected to show an optical effect caused by the earth's passage through the ether, but failed to show it. From 1887 until the 1930s, the experiment was repeated under various conditions, in persistent but unsuccessful attempts to show that the anticipated effect was present.

Albert A. Michelson, born in Poland in 1852, came to the United States as a child. After high school in San Francisco he was recommended for a special appointment to the U.S. Naval Academy. Ulysses S. Grant himself interviewed him at the White House. At Annapolis, Michelson showed great ability in the sciences, leading his class in optics. He became an instructor, and found an improved way of measuring the speed of light. Hitherto the best method had been devised by Jean Bernard Foucault, known today for demonstrating the rotation of the Earth with a large pendulum.

In 1879, Michelson carried out a detailed investigation of the speed of light, with a line of sight 2000 feet long across the Severn River at Annapolis. He communicated his methods and results to Simon Newcomb, president of the American Association for the Advancement of Science.

Impressed, Newcomb persuaded the Academy to allow Michelson to join him at the Naval Almanac Office.[2]

At about the same time, James Clerk Maxwell wrote to the same office, inquiring about the possibility of measuring the Earth's motion through the ether. A long series of investigations in the previous century had established beyond doubt that light is a wave form, implying the existence of a medium for it to wave in. By the latter half of the 19th century, its existence was regarded as certain.

The ether was thought of as a uniform, attenuated substance that filled the entirety of space. It was assumed to be "isotropic," or the same in all directions, and its parts were regarded as stationary in relation to each other. Often it was called the fixed ether. It would therefore constitute an immobile background against which the "absolute" motions of celestial bodies could be demonstrated. Therefore the Earth's passage through it could be measured.

Although *an* ether was needed to constitute the medium for electromagnetic waves, its other properties—its homogeneous, uniform, fixed character—were all assumed with little evidence. Yet an ether with different properties could easily be imagined. And just such an alternative medium is central to the argument of this book.

In an article for the *Encyclopedia Britannica*, published in 1875, Maxwell discussed a possible experiment to detect the ether. It would be difficult to carry out, however, because it would involve measuring something very small: a time interval proportional to "the square of the ratio of the Earth's velocity to that of light."

At about that time Michelson took time off for the equivalent of graduate studies. He knew about Maxwell's proposal, and pondered its technical requirements. Then he went to Berlin, where he worked under Hermann von Helmholtz. Alexander Graham Bell, frustrated by his own difficulties in raising funds for the telephone, gave Michelson a grant to proceed with the work.

In his Encyclopedia article, Clerk Maxwell had written:

> If it were possible to determine the velocity of light by observing the time it takes [for light] to travel between one station and another on the earth's surface, we might, by comparing the observed velocities in opposite directions, determine the velocity of the ether with respect to these terrestrial stations.[3]

If a light beam is sent from *A* to *B*, and the time taken is recorded; and then compared with the time for the beam's return, the Earth's motion through the ether could be demonstrated. During the time taken for the light beam's round trip, the light would necessarily move both with, and against, the earth's motion through the ether. If the light was sent in the same direction as the earth's motion through the ether, then the time for the light beam's return would be slightly shorter than for its outward journey. The observer and his apparatus would be moving to meet the returning beam and so its measured speed would be higher than that of the beam on its outward path.

One-way Speed of Light

But there was a problem: how to determine the one-way speed of light. That depends on knowing that two remote clocks are perfectly synchronized. And it is difficult, perhaps impossible, to know that they *are* synchronized without knowing the speed of light measured in one direction. Experimenters could send a light beam to a mirror and note the instant of its return. But if they assume that the time taken for the beam to return is half the total time, they are already assuming that the light speed is the same in both directions. But the purpose of the exercise is to find out if the speed in one direction is any different from the speed in the other.

There is a solution, however. We do know that if a beam of light is going against the ether wind in one direction, and with it in the other, the double journey will take slightly longer than if there is no ether wind at all. How can we measure that small increase? It was here that Michelson had his inspired idea. An experimenter could compare the round-trip time taken by one light beam with the round-trip time taken by another traveling at right angles to the first.

The best analogy is to a swimmer crossing a river with a current. It can be shown by simple geometry that the time taken to cross a river in both directions will be slightly less than the time taken to swim up and downstream, over a distance equal to the double journey across the river. The swimmer struggling upstream loses slightly more time that he gains when returning downstream with the current helping him. Michelson himself was the first to put it this way, in a letter to his own children:

> Two beams of light race against each other, like two swimmers, one struggling upstream and back, while the other, covering the same distance, just crossing the river and returns. The second swimmer will always win, *if there is any current in the river.*[4]

The underlying assumption was that the "ether wind" would be generated by the orbiting Earth. It moves "through" this ether (it was assumed) at about 18.5 miles per second. But light goes ten thousand times faster; at about 186,000 miles per second.

But because the experiment required that the time taken by the back and forth journey of the light beam be compared with that of another beam going at right angles to the first, the anticipated effect was much smaller still. The fraction 1/10,000 would have to be squared, giving us one part in a hundred million. The difference in the time taken by the two light beams would be "only about one hundred millionth part of the whole time of transmission," Clerk Maxwell wrote in his encyclopedia article. He thought this would be "quite insensible," or undetectable.

Michelson, a great experimentalist, devised an instrument capable of detecting it. It made use of the interference pattern produced by overlapping light beams, and was known as an interferometer for that reason. A beam of light reaches a half-silvered diagonal mirror in the center of the apparatus, and this allows some light to go through in a straight line, while the rest of the light is deflected through 90 degrees. Both beams are then reflected back by mirrors, and are rejoined and observed through an eyepiece. A *New York Times* writer said that Michelson had split a beam of light and raced "the halves against each another."[5]

The wave nature of light ensures that the reunited beams "interfere" with one another, as the British experimentalist Thomas Young had demonstrated almost a century earlier. This would appear as an array of light and dark fringes visible in the eyepiece. Where the crest of one light wave coincided with the crest of the other, the two would be reinforced, and a bright band would appear. But next to it the crest of one wave would coincide with the trough of the other, and there the two would cancel each other, creating a band of darkness. The discovery of these alternating fringes was convincing evidence for the wave nature of light.

Banesh Hoffmann, a colleague of Einstein's, described the design this way: "Michelson solved the problem of measuring a very small *time interval* by converting it into a *distance*: the distance traveled by light in that short time. The light and dark interference fringes "in effect allowed [Michelson] to measure that small distance by using the wave length of light as a yard stick."[6]

Almost everyone was confident that the ether existed, but the direction from which the ether-wind blew was less certain. It was not necessarily the direction of the Earth in its orbit. The sun itself was moving through the galaxy at a high speed, and with it the solar system. So it was difficult to say what the resultant direction of the apparatus might be, relative to the ether. The Earth's rotation would complicate matters, because six hours after one observation, the Earth would have turned through 90 degrees. By then the ether would be approaching the apparatus from a different direction.

Nonetheless, if the apparatus itself were rotated in the course of the experiment, the paths of light would be changed, relative to the Earth's orbital direction. This should produce a shift in the position of the fringes. In relation to a pointer fixed to the eyepiece, a particular fringe would move slightly to one side.

Leo Sartori explains this clearly in his *Understanding Relativity*. Michelson had "no way of knowing how the arms of his instrument were oriented," relative to the ether wind. But as the instrument was rotated, the emitted beam of light would at some point be in the direction of the ether flow. Then, after an additional rotation of the instrument itself through 90 degrees, the two arms would have changed places.

"One expects, therefore, that as the interferometer is rotated the fringe patterns will shift back and forth," Sartori wrote. "By measuring the maximum shift, Michelson expected to determine [the velocity of the Earth with respect to the ether]."[7]

In the winter of 1880-81, Michelson set up the apparatus in a basement at the University of Berlin. But even small movements near the lab caused the fringes to shake. Helmholtz suggested that it might be better for Michelson to wait until he returned to America, "as he doubted if they had the facilities for carrying out such experiments."[8] Eventually, they moved the whole operation to an observatory in Potsdam, 30 miles away.

Here, Michelson wrote, the fringes "were sufficiently quiet to measure, but so extraordinarily sensitive was the instrument that the stamping on the pavement about 100 meters from the observatory, made the fringes disappear entirely!"[9]

Michelson expected to find a fringe shift of about 0.08 of a wave length of light. But he was unable to discern any significant shift at all. Later, he learned that his calculations had been in error. With that error removed, the expected fringe-shift was only half of what he had assumed.

Michelson spent time in Heidelberg, where he met Prof. Wilhelm Bunsen, the inventor of the Bunsen burner. From him, Michelson learned that each element gave off its own spectrum. Monochromatic light would make it much easier to detect the fringes, and later Michelson used the yellow light given off by sodium when salt is heated in a flame. He spent a year in Paris, at that time probably the center of the scientific world. Andre Potier and Hendrik Lorentz discovered the error in his Potsdam calculations. Lorentz would soon be regarded as the most eminent physicist in the world, and we shall hear more of him.

"To see if light travels with the same velocity..."

The following year, Michelson obtained a position at the Case School of Applied Science in Cleveland. It must have been a comedown from Paris and Heidelberg. With his earlier error, and other room for improvement, Michelson resolved to repeat his experiment. He found a collaborator, Edward W. Morley, a professor of chemistry at nearby Western Reserve College. By adding mirrors to the table top, the light path was increased by a factor of ten. The expected fringe-shift should increase commensurately.

In 1887, Morley wrote to his father that "Michelson and I have begun a new experiment. It is to see if light travels with the same velocity in all directions," which was as succinct a way as any of describing it. "We shall have to make observations for a few minutes every month for a year," Morley added.

The optical parts of their equipment were mounted on a bed of stone, five feet square, and this in turn was floated in 200 pounds of mercury. It acted as a shock absorber, allowing the apparatus to be rotated smoothly without vibrations. The mercury consumed most of the grant from the National Academy of Sciences. In his fascinating account of the experiment in *The Ethereal Aether*, the historian Loyd Swenson wrote:

> By a gentle push of the observer's hand, the apparatus could be made to rotate very slowly, going through one complete turn in about six minutes. The observer, once his fringes could be adjusted for best 'seeing' and the block had started revolving on its almost frictionless liquid bearings, need not touch the apparatus at all, but could merely walk around with it and watch for any shift of the interference bands past a fiducial mark in his field of view.[10]

Finally, in July 1887, all was ready. "At noon on July 8, 9, and 11, and for one hour in the evening of July 8, 9, and 12, Michelson and Morley performed the simple yet amazing observations which were eventually to immortalize them," Swenson wrote. "Michelson walked the circuit and called off his estimates of fringe shifts at each of sixteen equidistant compass points, while, usually, Morley sat by and recorded the data. Their entire series of final observations consisted of only 36 turns of the interferometer, covering only six hours' duration over a five-day period in the summer of 1887. If Dayton C. Miller's history [published in 1933] can be trusted, and there is no reason to doubt it, they 'never repeated the ether-drift experiment at any other time, notwithstanding many printed statements to the contrary'." [11]

With the new apparatus, the expected fringe shift was 0.4 of a wave-length. But Michelson saw at most a shift of one hundredth of a wave-length. In their published paper, "On the Relative Motion of the Earth and the Luminiferous Ether" Michelson and Morley concluded:

> if there is any displacement due to the relative motion of the earth
> and the luminiferous ether, this cannot be much greater than 0.01 of
> the distance between the fringes . . . The relative velocity of the
> earth and the ether is probably less than one sixth the earth's orbital
> velocity, and certainly less than a fourth . . . If there be any relative
> motion between the earth and the luminiferous ether, it must be
> small. [12]

Notice that Michelson did not abandon the ether. He assumed that its velocity relative to the apparatus was much smaller than expected. To the end of his life—he died in 1931—he didn't change his mind and continued to believe that the ether was real. In his *Studies in Optics*, published in 1927, Michelson asked: "Without a medium, how can the propagation of light waves be explained?"

In 1924, he did a more elaborate experiment with Henry G. Gale of the University of Chicago. It was intended to test the theory that the much slower rotational (as opposed to the orbital) velocity of the earth generated a fringe-shift. This time he did find one. We shall return to this important and overlooked experiment in chapter 14. Michelson wrote in *Studies in Optics*:

> It is to be hoped that the theory [of relativity] may be reconciled with
> the existence of a medium, either by modifying the theory, or more
> probably, by attributing the requisite properties to the ether; for

example, allowing changes in its properties (dielectric constant, for example), due to the presence of a gravitational field.[13]

Michelson's comments are not entirely clear, but Petr Beckmann's theory was based on something similar. I shall outline his theory later, but a brief preview here will allow readers to visualize his alternative right away.

Translation and Rotation

In Beckmann's theory there is a luminiferous medium and it is equivalent to the local gravitational field. Because the Earth, orbiting the Sun, carries its gravitational field with it, no relative motion between the gravitational field and the orbiting Earth is to be expected.

But as the Earth rotates, it does so "within" its gravitational field. By analogy, when a woman with a circular waist wearing a hoop skirt spins around, or pirouettes, and friction is minimal, the skirt will not rotate with her. Analogously, an "ether drift" caused by the Earth's *rotation* should exist. But because the Earth's rotational velocity is much smaller than its orbital velocity, the effect that Beckmann predicts is much smaller than what Michelson expected to see. At mid-latitudes, it would be about ten thousand times smaller. Michelson's instrument, built in the 1880s, could not possibly have detected it. That is Beckmann's idea in a nutshell.

Michelson left the Case School of Applied Science in 1889. He moved first to Clark University and then to the University of Chicago. He was replaced at Case by Dayton C. Miller, who became Morley's close friend. They attended the Paris Exposition of 1900 and there met Lord Kelvin, who "strongly urged" them to repeat the ether-drift experiment. Lorentz was also lecturing at Leiden University about the Michelson-Morley experiment.[14]

There were various interpretations, possibilities and criticisms of the famous experiment. Michelson had at one point said they would make observations quarterly. After three months, the Earth would be moving in a direction 90 degrees different from its initial direction. But all their readings were made within a few days.

In their 1887 paper, Michelson and Morley had suggested that fringe shifts might more easily be detected at a greater height. The idea here was that the ether might be "entrained" by the earth's motion, or swept along with the earth. This entrainment might be less effective at a higher altitude. In 1905, therefore, Morley and Miller collaborated on a new and still more accurate version of the experiment, on Euclid (later Cleveland) Heights, near Lake Erie.

Einstein himself went to Case in May, 1921, visited the site of the classic Michelson-Morley experiment, and urged Dayton Miller to keep looking.[15] He did, and regularly reported finding a fringe shift. But if it was real, and not produced by confounding factors such as temperature fluctuations, it was much smaller than the Maxwellian ether required.

In 1920, George Ellery Hale, the director of Mt. Wilson Observatory in California, invited Miller to repeat the experiment on top of Mt. Wilson. By 1924, when he was president of the American Physical Society, Miller had concluded that "the effects were shown to be real and systematic, beyond any question."[16] But the effect was only 30 percent of what was expected, and the doubts persisted.

In the end, Miller's interpretation, that the fringe shift was real, was not accepted. It was assumed that all the experiments, whether by Michelson or Miller, and whether conducted in basements or on mountain tops, had shown a "null result." Further, these experiments were taken to have disproved the ether hypothesis.

Michelson was awarded the Nobel Prize in Physics in 1907— the first American scientist to receive it. He was honored not for his ether-drift experiment but for another collaboration with Morley, this one to see whether wave lengths of light could provide a standard unit of length.[17] Some historians have concluded that Michelson was in effect recognized for his perfection of the interferometer. Its precision was way ahead of anything achieved by others at the time, and for many years to come.

Michelson Papers Discarded

Although he was a major figure in American science, little discernible research has been done on Michelson's papers in the almost 80 years since his death. Sadly, too, valuable material in Michelson's office in the Ryerson Laboratory at the University of Chicago seem to have been thrown out after his death. In *The Master of Light*, his daughter Dorothy Michelson Livingston wrote:

> In time, the Manhattan Project moved into Ryerson and all material not immediately pertinent to the creation of the atomic pile was

thrown out.   Ruling engine records, polarization of light records, butterfly and insect specimens, prisms, gratings, books, notebooks, and loose-leaf records of his work were all stolen or lost.

Tom O'Donnell showed me the spot where the contents of Michelson's desk were dumped.   Students rifling the letters had found a number of canceled checks bearing his signature, which were selling for a fair price even then.   Tom swears that there were letters from Röntgen, Rayleigh, Kelvin, Larmor, Lodge, Gibbs, and many others, which were destroyed before the scavengers could lay their hands on them.   This is why in so many instances I have found Michelson's letters in the files of these men, but have not found their answers, unless by good fortune they were methodical enough to make duplicates, a laborious process before the days of typewriters and copying machines.[18]

The bulk of Michelson's remaining papers are preserved at the U.S. Naval Academy in Annapolis today; some material is at the University of Chicago, some at Case Western Reserve and perhaps at the Mount Wilson Institute.   One hopes that before too many more years elapse researchers will take an interest.

His opposition to relativity is downplayed, and today it is hardly known.   Dorothy Livingston minimizes her father's dissent, although she acknowledges it.[19] It may be that undiscovered material among Michelson's surviving papers will shed new light on these matters.

In an introduction to Loyd Swenson's book, Gerald Holton said that Michelson's interferometer had played a historical role "analogous to Galileo's telescope."[20] Just as the telescope had "cast fatal doubt on the physics of its time," so did the interferometer.   It is an interesting comparison.   The parallel breaks down, however, in that Galileo endorsed the new worldview ushered in by the telescope, whereas Michelson remained unreconciled to the Einsteinian worldview, from which the ether would be banished and in which waves no longer needed a medium to wave in.

A centennial symposium on the Michelson-Morley experiment was held at Cleveland in 1987.   One of the participants was Dorothy Livingston.   Her remarks, published by the American Institute of Physics, contain comments rarely encountered in the Einstein literature:

In 1905, when [Einstein] made his great thesis, he was disappointed that he didn't get instant recognition from four people: Ernst Mach, H. A. Lorentz, Poincaré and Michelson.   None of them came

forward in 1905 and said 'this is it.' Well, years later [Einstein] came
to America when he was widely recognized and feted from one end
of the country to the other. He showed a certain coldness at
meetings. My father and he would meet a various scientific
gatherings and he was, you know, chilly. And of course Michelson
never liked his theory, so that was another point. So they never
really spoke then.[21]

None of those four "came forward in 1905"—or at any time, she
might have added. Nonetheless, there was a personal reconciliation
between Michelson and Einstein:

"Then my father retired from Chicago to California, and he was
working up on Mt. Wilson when Einstein appeared out there,"
Dorothy Livingston continued.

And in the evening of his life he was very happy to talk with
Einstein. My father was failing in health and he was really quite ill
at the end and Einstein used to come to the house. I was there when
he came. My father would play him a tune on the violin and he
would play the violin. Then father would get out some water colors
that he had been making of California, and the whole friendship was
really sealed in a beautiful way.[21]

Notes: Chapter 3

[1]   Gerald Holton, *Thematic Origins of Scientific Thought*, revised ed. Harvard, 1988. Chs. 6-8.

[2]   The principal sources for this chapter are Loyd S. Swenson, *The Ethereal Aether*, University of Texas, 1972; and Dorothy Michelson Livingston, *The Master of Light: A Biography of Albert A. Michelson*, Charles Scribner's, N.Y., 1973.

[3]   Maxwell, "Ether," *Britannica*, op. cit.

[4]   Dorothy Livingston, p. 77.

[5]   *New York Times*, Nov 20, 1927, cited in Swenson, p. 220.

[6]   Banesh Hoffmann, *Roots of Relativity*, p. 76 (Michelson re. Helmholtz, Livingston, p. 75.)

[7]   Leo Sartori, *Understanding Relativity: A Simplified Approach to Einstein's Theories*, Univ. of California Press, 1996, pp. 36-37.

[8]   Dorothy Livingston, p. 75

[9]   Livingston, p.78-9; Michelson (1881) in *American Journal of Science*, v. 22, no.128.

[10]   Swenson, p.93.

[11]   Swenson, pp.93-94.

[12]   Michelson-Morley (1887) *Am. Journal of Science*, v 34, Nov. 1887.

[13]   A. A. Michelson, *Studies in Optics*, Dover, N.Y. 1995, pp 161-62; first published by University of Chicago, 1927.

[14]   Swenson, p.195.

[15]   Swenson, p.141, 142.

[16]   Swenson, p. 206 et seq.

[17]   Albert E. Moyer, "Michelson in 1887," *Physics Today*, May 1987, p.50.

[18]   Dorothy Livingston, p.340.

[19]   Dorothy Livingston, p.334.

[20]   Gerald Holton, introduction to Swenson, p. xx.

[21]   Dorothy Livingston, "Reminiscences of My Father," in *Modern Physics in America: A Michelson-Morley Centennial Symposium*, American Institute of Physics, N.Y., 1988, p. 24.

Chapter 4. Lorentz and Poincaré

Scientists in the late 19th century were "stunned" by the Michelson-Morley result, Jeremy Bernstein said. J. Robert Oppenheimer noted its "traumatic character," while Einstein himself wrote that it had "placed [physicists] in greatest embarrassment."[1] It led to "one of the most dramatic situations in the history of science," wrote Einstein and Leopold Infeld.[2]

Earlier experimenters had tried to detect the Earth's motion through the ether. No such effects had been seen, but the equipment had been designed in the Napoleonic era, so the predicted effects were assumed to be beyond the instruments' capacities.

But Michelson's interferometer should have been able to do the job. His result therefore implied some basic misconception in the underlying theory. It gave rise to one of those moments when the prevailing physical "paradigm" was no longer working, although it had given satisfaction for a century or more.[3]

Hendrik A. Lorentz (1853-1928) had paid close attention to all this. He held the chair of theoretical physics at the University of Leiden in Holland, and in 1902 shared the Nobel Prize in Physics with Pieter Zeeman for research into the influence of magnetism on radiation. He presided over the gatherings of the Solvay Congress, welcomed new ideas, and seems to have been a model scientist. The object of physical research, he said, "was to find simple basic principles from which all phenomena can be deduced."[4]

He got on well with everyone. Einstein congratulated Lorentz on his 70th birthday saying that he had found "deep consolation in your noble and outstanding personality. . . . To follow you on your path has been the most important content of my life." This was all the more impressive in that the two scientists held strongly opposed views "on some very fundamental and important issues," as A.J. Kox has written.[5] Lorentz had seemed to lay the groundwork for relativity, but he never accepted Einstein's theory.

Lorentz was initially at a loss to account for the Michelson-Morley result, but in the 1890s he proposed a theory in which material objects consisted of electrons, and as they passed through the ether, they were deformed. Michelson's null result could be explained if motion through the ether caused an object to contract, thereby accounting for the missing effect.[6]

But this was a "physics of desperation," Arthur I. Miller said.[7] One anticipated but unobserved effect was countered by another. So everything stayed the same. The hypothesis of contraction was "not justifiable by any electrodynamical facts," Einstein wrote, in a rare criticism of Lorentz.[8]

The idea of length-contraction had also been suggested by the Irish physicist George Fitzgerald., who sent a letter to *Science* in 1889, proposing that idea. At first neither Fitzgerald nor Lorentz knew if it had been published. The magazine had briefly gone out of existence, leaving Fitzgerald to suppose that his letter never saw print. The ever-scrupulous Lorentz made inquiries and duly credited Fitzgerald with priority.[9] The hypothesis is often referred to as the Fitzgerald-Lorentz contraction.

As the velocity (with respect to the ether) increases so does the contraction. The measuring instruments would also contract, so the fringe shift anticipated by Michelson, although greater at higher speeds, would never appear. With a quotation from *Through the Looking Glass*, Eddington questioned whether nature would both generate an ether wind and then go to such lengths to hide it.[10]

Lorentz's contraction formula was retained by Einstein in his theory of relativity. In the next chapter, this will be described from Einstein's point of view, showing how the idea of contraction became a mainstay of special relativity. But there was also a key difference. In Lorentz's theory, the objects themselves physically contract as a result of their passage through the ether. There was a real material cause. In Einstein's theory, *space* contracts (and *time* expands) in reference frames that are moving with *respect to the observer*. Motion itself generates an adjustment of space and time.

The Lorentz formula is such that objects contract (in the direction of motion) only to a very small extent until their speed reaches an appreciable fraction of the speed of light. The orbiting Earth, for example, "would be contracted by a mere six centimeters or so," Banesh Hoffmann wrote.

In 1895, Lorentz published his theory in detail, stating that the arms of the interferometer contract in the direction of the earth's motion through the ether. He regarded the contraction as real and "dynamic" — caused by physical interactions with the ether.

At the turn of the century the French mathematician and physicist Henri Poincaré criticized the ad hoc character of the various attempts to measure the earth's motion through the ether. By then, there had been added to length contraction a further proposal of a "local time". But there should be a more general explanation, Poincaré thought. He suggested refinements and improvements, which Lorentz then incorporated in a more thorough statement, published in 1904.

Henri Poincaré

Poincaré seemed close to formulating the theory of relativity himself. In a lecture at the Sorbonne in 1899 he said it was probable "that optical phenomena depend only on the relative motions of the material bodies, luminous sources and optical apparatus concerned," and that absolute motion would prove to be undetectable in principle.

"A new principle would thus be introduced into physics, which would resemble the Second Law of Thermodynamics," Edmund Whittaker commented, in his *History of the Theories of Aether and Electricity*. Such a principle would assert "*the impossibility of doing something*: in this case the impossibility of determining the velocity of the earth relative to the aether."[11]

In *Science and Hypothesis* (1902) Poincaré referred to the "principle of relativity" for the first time. And in 1904, in a speech in St. Louis, he formulated the principle exactly as Einstein later used it:

> The laws of physical phenomena should be the same for a stationary observer as for an observer carried along in a uniform motion of translation; so that we have not and can not have any means of discerning whether or not we are carried along in such a motion.[12]

He discussed the synchronization of clocks using a method similar to that proposed by Einstein. He even added that we might have to construct a new mechanics, "where, inertia increasing with velocity, the velocity of light would become an impassable limit."

In fact, Leo Sartori wrote, Poincaré "articulated many of the central concepts of relativity, some of them before Einstein."[12]

But they were further apart than these similarities suggest. So were Einstein and Lorentz. Einstein's advocates are right to insist that special relativity was his alone. Both Lorentz and Poincaré retained the ether, and neither argued that the speed of light is invariant. Poincaré did express doubts about the ether, but he continued to assign it an important role. In a review article in 1908 he said: "the universe contains electrons, ether and nothing else."[13] In 1912, the year of his death, he published a paper entitled "the Relation between Ether and Matter."

Poincaré did not mention Einstein's relativity between its introduction and his own death in 1912. Relations between the two men seemed chilly, in contrast to Einstein's warm friendship with Lorentz. "It is apparent that Poincaré was tantalizingly close to a theory of relativity," Sartori wrote. "But he either did not see the all-important final step or was not bold enough to take it."[14]

Stanley Goldberg takes a different view. We are reduced to speculation, because Poincaré died suddenly at the age of 60. He didn't write anything about Einstein's relativity, but hardly anyone in France did before 1912. Everything we know about Poincaré's character "belies a motive as petty as jealousy," Goldberg writes. He adds that Poincaré and Lorentz had been working on a comprehensive theory of electrons which was going to subsume all of physics. Einstein's second postulate, about the speed of light, "must have seemed artificial."[15]

Lorentzian contraction had a real physical cause. But for Einstein, Sartori wrote, it was an inherent property of space and time:

> The distance between two bodies is shortened when it is measured
> by observers for whom the bodies are in motion, even if no matter
> occupies the space between them. The Lorentz model cannot
> account for this contraction of 'empty space'.[16]

Indeed it cannot. Maybe that is because the contraction of empty space caused by the motion of an observer relative to that space must have seemed close to an absurdity. Yet, as we shall see, we must either accept that it is true or reject the theory of relativity.

In a letter to Einstein in 1915 Lorentz reiterated his preference for retaining the ether. In fact, he "never embraced Einstein's 1905 reinterpretation of the equations of his [Lorentz's] electron theory," Russell McCormmach wrote in his article on Lorentz in the *Dictionary of Scientific Biography*. "To the end of his life he believed that the ether was a reality and that absolute space and time were meaningful concepts."[17]

In his last public appearance, a year before his death, Lorentz attended a conference in Pasadena, California, on the Michelson-Morley experiment. It was still under investigation 40 years later. Michelson himself was present. As to time and space, Lorentz said on that occasion, "there existed for me only this one true time."[18]

After the total eclipse confirmed the bending of starlight and Einstein's general relativity, Lorentz wrote an article later published as a small book by Brentano's, *The Einstein Theory of Relativity: A Concise Statement.* He said something that seemed to hint at Petr Beckmann's ideas published almost 60 years later.

> It is not necessary to give up entirely even the ether. Many natural philosophers find satisfaction in the idea of a material intermediate substance in which the vibrations of light take place, and they will very probably be all the more inclined to imagine such a medium when they learn that, according to the Einstein theory, gravitation itself does not spread instantaneously, but with a velocity that at first estimate may be compared with that of light.

Speculation about the ether, Lorentz went on, had hoped to arrive at a "clear statement of electromagnetic phenomena and also of the functioning of gravitation." It was possible that in the future this road, "abandoned at present, will once more be followed with good results, if only because it can lead to the thinking out of new experimental tests."[19]

Within months of the book's publication, Einstein gave a lecture at Leiden, with Lorentz in attendance. Einstein argued that a revival of the ether was perhaps overdue, bearing in mind that his general theory of relativity was itself a gravitational theory.[20] This development, rarely noted, and its bearing on Petr Beckmann's ideas, will be discussed in chapter 21.

Notes: Chapter 4

[1]   Bernstein, *Einstein*, Penguin, 1976, p. 52; J. Robert Oppenheimer, *The Flying Trapeze: Three Crises for Physicists*, Oxford, 1964, p. 14; Gerald Holton, *Thematic Origins*, p. 478.

[2]   Einstein and Infeld, *Evolution of Physics*, Simon and Schuster, N.Y. 1938, p.183, 184.

[3]   Thomas Kuhn, *The Structure of Scientific Revolutions*, 2nd ed. Univ. of Chicago, 1970.

[4]   Russell McCormmach, "Hendrik A. Lorentz," *Dictionary of Scientific Biography*, 1970, v. 8, p. 490.

[5]   A.J. Kox, "Einstein and Lorentz: More than Just Good Colleagues," *Einstein in Context*, ed. Mara Beller et al, Cambridge, 1993, p. 43, 50.

[6]   Arthur Eddington, *The Nature of the Physical World*, The Macmillan Co. 1928, p. 7.

[7]   Arthur I. Miller, *Albert Einstein's Special Theory of Relativity*, Springer 1998, p.28.

[8]   Albert Einstein, *The Special and the General Theory*, 1917, p.51.

[9]   Banesh Hoffmann, *Relativity and its Roots*, Scientific American Books, 1983, p.82.

[10]   Eddington, op. cit. p. 28.

[11]   Edmund Whittaker, *A History of the Theories of Aether and Electricity*, 2 vols (1953), Harper Torchbook, v. 2, p. 30.

[12]   Leo Sartori, *Understanding Relativity*, pp. 128-130.

[13]   Sartori, p.132.

[14]   Sartori, p.132.

[15]   Stanley Goldberg, *Understanding Relativity*, Birkhauser, Boston, 1984, p. 216.

[16]   Sartori, 87-88.

[17]   *Dictionary of Scientific Biography*, v. 8, p. 498.

[18]   A. A. Michelson et al., "Conference on the Michelson-Morley Experiment, Held at the Mt. Wilson Observatory, Pasadena, California, Feb. 4, 5, 1927," *Astrophysical Journal*, December, 1928.

[19]   H.A. Lorentz, *The Einstein Theory of Relativity: A Concise Statement*, Brentano's, N.Y., 1920, 60-62.

[20]   Albert Einstein, *Essays in Science*, Philosophical Library, 1934, 98-111.

Chapter 5. The Special Theory of Relativity

The special theory was Einstein's solution to the problem that arose as a result of the "unsuccessful attempts to detect a motion of the earth relative to the light medium," to use his own words in 1905.[1] He didn't single out the Michelson-Morley experiment, but almost certainly he had it in mind. This itself is disputed, and I explore that later. But it is of secondary importance. More important is to discover what Einstein's theory is claiming.

In outlining his theory, Einstein proceeded by the method of postulates. Certain propositions are assumed to be true. Einstein says, in effect, "let us assume that they are true." He then works out their consequences. If the (two) postulates are true, various physical phenomena should be observed. They amount to predictions of the theory. If they are observed, then Einstein can claim that his theory has been confirmed. Observations in conflict with those predictions, on the other hand, will tend to falsify the theory.

That is the perfectly conventional method that Einstein uses. He states his theory, predicts its consequences, and looks to see if the physical world corroborates them.

The core of his theory is found within five sentences early in his paper, "On the Electrodynamics of Moving Bodies." The passage is written in plain language, mostly, with little technical jargon. But we need to be warned that it is less straightforward than it appears. At one point Einstein doesn't quite say what he means, and that has been the source of much confusion. If we are to understand relativity, it is essential to know what is going on in this passage. Everything else in the theory follows from it.

> ... [N]ot only the phenomena of mechanics but also those of electrodynamics have no properties that correspond to the concept of absolute rest. Rather, the same laws of electrodynamics and optics will be valid for all coordinate system in which the equations of mechanics hold, as has already been shown for quantities of the first order. We shall raise this conjecture (whose content will hereafter be called the "principle of relativity") to the status of a postulate and shall also introduce another postulate which is only seemingly

incompatible with it, namely that light always propagates in empty space with a definite velocity V that is independent of the state of motion of the emitting body. These two postulates suffice for the attainment of a simple and consistent electrodynamics of moving bodies based on Maxwell's theory for bodies at rest. The introduction of a 'light ether' will prove to be superfluous, inasmuch as the view to be developed here will not require a 'space at absolute rest' endowed with special properties... [2]

In his book *Understanding Relativity*, Leo Sartori says that "all of special relativity follows by logical deduction from these two postulates."[3] It is an important point and rarely stated so plainly. Students soon find themselves grappling with the proposition that there is no universal time, for example, or that the simultaneity of clocks in relative motion cannot be established. They learn also that these things are somehow entailed by relativity.

They are, but we need to know that they are *deductions from Einstein's postulates.* They were not independently observed and built into the theory for that reason. If for any reason we reject either postulate, then non-simultaneity and a multiplicity of times will also disappear. We will no longer have to ponder them. They are not empirical realities that have been independently verified.

The first postulate can be read as a summary statement of the theory of relativity itself. We have already discussed it earlier, but here it is again, extracted from the passage above.

... not only the phenomena of mechanics but also those of electrodynamics have no properties that correspond to the concept of absolute rest. Rather, the same laws of electrodynamics and optics will be valid for all coordinate systems in which the equations of mechanics hold ...

What Einstein is saying is that inside a smoothly moving railway carriage, the phenomena of electricity and light will no more be affected by the motion of the carriage than the passengers are, or any mechanical experiments that they might perform. It extends to *all* physical phenomena the observations that Galileo had already made about mechanical phenomena. So the first postulate simply says: Let us *assume* that this claim is true.

In the first place, the postulate has the merit of being consistent with the Michelson-Morley "null result." It had failed to detect the effect of motion on light waves, possibly because there *was* no such effect. (That is the usual interpretation of the experiment.) Another possibility was that the effect was present but too small for Michelson's equipment to detect.

Anyway, in his first postulate Einstein assumes that the effect was not there. Michelson showed that moving his apparatus through the ether had no effect, and the First Postulate predicted that.

But there was also a problem with this postulate, on its own. It was in conflict with the prevailing theory of electromagnetism. Motion through the light medium *should* have produced an effect, as just about everyone at the time expected it would. That it had not done so suggested that something quite basic in physical theory might be wrong.

Therefore, Einstein proposed a second postulate, worded as follows. (The letter V was by convention changed to the more familiar c a year or two after his paper was published.)

> Light always propagates in empty space with a definite velocity V that is independent of the state of motion of the emitting body.

Immediately following this, Einstein went on to say that these two postulates would "suffice for the attainment of a simple and consistent electrodynamics of moving bodies." (We won't need any more postulates, he was saying.) Then, in a casual aside, he added that "the introduction of a light ether will prove to be superfluous."

Confusion may already be setting in, so here is a brief recap:

First of all, linear, unaccelerated motion doesn't affect the laws of mechanics—as was known to Newton and Galileo. Within the hold of a smoothly sailing ship, a sailor lacking port holes cannot tell whether he is moving or not. But by the 19th century electromagnetic theory predicted that smooth motion *would* generate measurable effects for electricity and light. Motion through the light medium *should* produce visible effects. But Michelson had not found them. Lorentz had suggested an explanation: motion through the ether caused the measuring equipment itself to contract in the direction of motion, and this exactly offset the anticipated effect.

In his new theory, then, Einstein was saying there really was no effect. He was claiming that the laws of electromagnetism are as indifferent to motion as are the laws of mechanics. He achieved this parsimonious and ostensibly desirable outcome with the help of his second postulate. This is where we have to pay careful attention.

The second postulate lies at the heart of the mystery of special relativity. It blandly tells us something that we have all heard—that the speed of light is a constant—but Einstein was nonetheless saying something that tends to remain opaque, sometimes even to students of relativity. An important reason is that Einstein himself stated his own postulate in a misleading way.

Einstein's Stage Magic

We must approach the second postulate as circumspectly as we would the performance of a conjuror or magician. The man pulls a rabbit out of a hat in front of our eyes, and we know something isn't as it appears. But we can't quite see what it is.

But don't take my word for it. Let us hear from one of his greatest admirers and best expositors, Banesh Hoffmann. For a while he was Einstein's colleague at Princeton's Institute for Advanced Studies and later his biographer. He cannot be suspected of even a trace of heresy. He is the best known commentator to have drawn attention to Einstein's brilliant stage magic.

Here is what Hoffmann says in *Albert Einstein: Creator and Rebel*. He is about to explain the inner workings of the special theory. But first he gives us this warning:

> Watch closely. It will be worth the effort. But be forewarned. As we follow the gist of Einstein's argument we shall find ourselves nodding in agreement, and later almost nodding in sleep, so obvious and unimportant will it seem. There will come a stage at which we shall barely be able to stifle a yawn. Beware. We shall by then have committed ourselves and it will be too late to avoid the jolt; for the beauty of Einstein's argument lies precisely in its seeming innocence.[4]

What does "we might commit ourselves" mean? He means that once we accept those two postulates, we shall have to accept their consequences. Then it will be "too late" to insist, as we may want to do, that what follows seems unacceptable. Heed the warning, therefore. Recall Leo Sartori's comment that "all of special relativity follows by logical deduction from these two postulates." The special theory is like a legal contract containing a tricky clause. Before signing on the dotted line, let us examine it with care.

If indeed there does turn out to be something wrong with the special theory, we can be sure that it is hidden in these postulates. A few years later, in 1912, Einstein said that "the theory of relativity is correct insofar as the two principles upon which it is based are correct."[5] That is a fair comment. In effect he is acknowledging the provisional nature of his own postulates.

Hoffmann went on to say—still in a cautionary vein—that Einstein's 1905 argument is based on "concepts of beguiling acceptability." Accept them, and we shall have "unknowingly committed ourselves to a staggering consequence."[6] He repeated a comparable warning in his later book *Relativity and Its Roots* (1983). Einstein's two postulates are "cunningly chosen," he wrote, for "each by itself seems harmless, yet the two together form an explosive mixture destined to rock the very foundations of science." In fact, the consequences that follow are "revolutionary."[7]

I agree with Hoffmann's analysis, excepting only the admiration that he bestows. For the use of "beguiling" procedures that only "seem" innocent to the reader is not normally regarded as an admirable modus operandi within science.

The Second Postulate

It seems plain enough—the speed of light is always the same "irrespective of the motion of the emitting body." But this formulation is far from straightforward. Our gratitude to Banesh Hoffmann, who put his finger on the problem:

> Einstein's second principle takes on the aspect of an utter triviality. For no matter how a light wave is started, once it is on its way it is carried by the ether at the standard speed with which waves are transmitted therein.[8]

In *Relativity and Its Roots*, Hoffmann expressed the same idea in a slightly different way.

> For if a source of light generates light waves in the ether, once the waves are launched they are no longer linked to their source; they are on their own, moving at the rate set by the elastic properties of the ether.[7]

The idea that a wave travels at a definite speed unaffected by the movement of its *source* was, and remains to this day, an everyday feature of wave theory.   It is something that was once taught in high-school physics.   Physicists reading Einstein's paper in 1905 must have considered the second postulate unremarkable— hardly worth postulating, in fact.

In the medium of air, the sound wave of a plane proceeds through the skies at about 750 miles per hour, whether the plane is traveling at 100 or 600 mph through that air.   Petr Beckmann would illustrate the point by saying that if a seagull skims over the sea and taps the water with the tip of a wing, the resulting wave proceeds at a speed that is unaffected by the speed of the gull.   The speed of sound in air is not an absolute, because it depends on air pressure; the speed of water waves depends on the depth of the water.   But in neither case is the speed affected by the speed of the wave source.

Einstein "extracts from the ether the essential that he needs," Hoffmann wrote.   Two sentences later the ether is whisked away, because it is now "superfluous." Here indeed we see the magician in action.   Einstein had taken as his second postulate "something inherent in the wave theory of light, even as he declares the idea of an ether superfluous." In so doing, Hoffmann added, he "gave a striking indication of the sureness of his physical intuition."

In that indulgent comment Hoffmann goes astray, surely. Einstein knew perfectly well that a light speed independent of the motion of the *source* was uncontroversial.   Physicists fully expected that.   But with the ether removed, we were in a very different world.

Without the ether, all we have is the source of light and the observer of the light; if *one* is moving, all we can say is that there is relative motion between source and observer.   It is no longer possible to say, in any absolute sense, *which* is moving.   Without the ether as physical substrate, the first postulate gains the upper hand.   It forces us to accept that if one thing is moving relative to another, and there is no medium, then any attempt to distinguish between the motion of the source and the motion of the observer is futile.

Revolution in Physics

Henceforth, therefore, without the ether, accepting the second postulate will oblige us to accept that the speed of light is a constant, not just irrespective of the source's motion, but also irrespective of the observer's.

And that does introduce a revolution into physics. It leads to Hoffmann's "staggering consequence." Move the source, and the speed of the wave is unaffected. Move the observer (in conventional wave theory), and the motion of the observer must be added to or subtracted from the speed of the wave, in order to know the speed with which the wave approaches the observer.

When Einstein said "source," then, what he really meant was "source or observer." We know he meant that because he plainly said so himself—some years later. In November 1919, following the immense publicity surrounding the confirmed bending of starlight near the sun, he wrote in an article for the *Times* of London:

> The second principle, on which the theory of relativity rests, is 'the principle of the constant velocity of light *in vacuo*.' This principle asserts that light *in vacuo* always has a definite velocity of propagation (independent of the state of motion of the observer or of the source of the light).[10]

I believe this was the first time that Einstein said plainly that the speed of light is a constant irrespective of the *observer's* motion.[11]

Einstein addressed the subject again in his popular account, *Relativity, The Special and the General Theory.* He ambiguously referred to "the constancy of the velocity of light,"[12] without explaining: constant with respect to what? He then had the audacity to continue: "Who would imagine that this simple law had plunged the conscientiously thoughtful physicist into the greatest intellectual difficulties?" He wondered "how these difficulties arise."[13] Yet he still had not plainly said that the velocity of light, in his theory, is assumed to be unaffected by the motion of the *observer*.

Think of it this way. From the constancy of the speed of light irrespective of the movement of the source (*with* an ether) Einstein had inferred the constancy of the speed of light, irrespective of the movement of the observer (*without* an ether).

Deformation of Space and Time

Why is this so important? The former is an everyday feature of wave theory. The latter undermines the fundamentals of physics—space and time.

By analogy, let us apply these ideas to sound waves and see how accepted physical theory treats them. Then we can move on to light.   For the sake of argument, assume we have a (stationary) vehicle with a siren.   Observers down the road measure the speed with which the siren's sound approaches them, and all agree that it is, say, 750 mph.   Now the vehicle moves forward (at a constant speed), and all observers continue to find that the speed of the approaching sound wave remains unchanged—unaffected by the motion of the source.   Sound waves behave just as Einstein said light waves do.   Their speed is "independent of the state of motion of the emitting body."

Now, we put observers in two cars down the road and they are moving either toward or away from the approaching sound wave. Both cars are moving at 50 miles per hour, with respect to the road. The one moving toward the sound source finds the siren wave approaching at 800 miles per hour, while the other measures the wave approaching at 700 miles per hour.   Common sense, physical theory and observation are all in agreement.   We simply add (or subtract) the observers' motion to (or from) the speed of the sound wave to find its speed relative to the observer.

But when it comes to measuring the speed of light, Einstein says, we don't add or subtract the observers' motion.   We assume— or rather, he postulates—that all observers, however they are moving (providing that motion is unaccelerated) will measure the light wave approaching at a uniform, constant speed, c.

How can this be?

There is of course an important distinction between the sound and light examples.   Sound waves are transmitted in the medium of air, so sound certainly has its "ether."   This means that the motion of the sound source relative to the ground is irrelevant.   For a sound wave (as Hoffmann noted) proceeds at its own speed, depending only the "elastic properties" of the medium (air).   It will be unaffected by the motion of the source—the vehicle with the siren.

In measuring light waves, however, we no longer have an ether; Einstein has banished it.   Therefore, the only speed we must deal with is the relative speed of the light source and the observer.   Let us assume we now have two moving vehicles with observers who are measuring the speed of an approaching beam of light.   One vehicle is moving toward the light wave at 100 mph, the other moving toward it at 50 mph.

If light waves behaved like sound waves, we would expect to add the speed of each vehicle to that of the light wave.   Since the speed of light is so enormous compared to the vehicles', the difference would be very small. It would be the speed of light in a vacuum, plus 100 mph in one case; plus 50 miles per hour in the other. (These additions are almost negligible, of course, compared with the nearly 500 million miles that light travels in an hour.)

Yet Einstein's second postulate decrees that any vehicle on the ground, however moving, in whatever direction at whatever speed, will record the light beam as approaching at an unvarying, constant speed, c. How can this be? Well, to be tiresomely repetitive, it has been postulated. For the sake of argument, then, we must proceed as though it is true. Speed is simply distance divided by time, so the required procedure, adopted by Einstein's theory, is to adjust space and time by an appropriate factor, so that distance divided by time always yields the same quotient, c.

The "appropriate factor" is itself determined by the speed at which the light source and the observer are approaching one another.

Both observers must find that, in the reference frame of the light source, as seen by them, space is foreshortened and time is dilated, but to a different extent for each observer. The greater the approach speed, the more space is said to contract, the more time is said to expand. Consequently, the adjusted distance divided by the adjusted time always yields the same quotient, c—the ever-constant speed of light, for both observers. And this will hold true for any number of observers who may be moving in relation to the light source.

Observer-Dependent Reality

Reality has become observer-dependent, as Petr Beckmann used to say, summarizing the principal reason why he was unable to accept relativity. Space and time become the handmaidens of a particular speed. They must henceforth "cater to" the speed of light, Beckmann said, forever adjusting themselves so that the one divided by the other yields the same constant, c.

The mathematical formulae, giving the extent to which these contractions and expansions are said to occur, were published by Hendrik A. Lorentz a few years before 1905. In relativity theory they are called the Lorentz Transformations.

Notice that all along we have been proceeding purely within the realm of logical deduction. Space contraction and time dilation are simply *dictated* by Einstein's second postulate, properly understood.

That is why Banesh Hoffmann warned us that once we accept those postulates, we set ourselves up for a "staggering consequence."

When the observer moves toward the *sound* wave, we simply add their speeds to find the speed of the approaching wave: 750 mph + 50 mph = 800 mph. That is called the Galilean transformation. But with light, things don't quite add up any more and the Galilean must be replaced by the Lorentz transformation.

Usually given as mathematical formulae, the Lorentz transformations lie at the heart of the special theory. They describe the extent to which space and time must be adjusted in the reference frame that is moving with respect to the observer. Notice that, in accordance with the first postulate, the observer's *own* reference frame can always be regarded as stationary, as long as we confine ourselves to non-accelerated motion (as special relativity dictates). Therefore, no changes in space or time are to be expected *within the observer's own frame*. It is always in the other reference frame that space is seen to be shrinking or time slowing down.

The Lorentz formulae are based on the Pythagorean Theorem. As they can look daunting to laymen I omit them here. They are uncontroversial in themselves—no one claims that mathematical errors are involved in the theory; the math never rises above high-school algebra anyway. Again, if there is any error, it's in the postulates, not in their mathematical elaboration.

These deduced adjustments or transformations of space and time amount to predictions of relativity theory. Have they in fact been observed, experimentally? That is a crucial question, and I shall address it in later chapters. But before doing so, I ask the reader to consider how bizarre it is even to entertain such an idea: *Because I move, your watch slows down.*

Alpha and Omega

Time and space are the alpha and the omega of physics. They are to physics what the clock and the yard lines are to football. Yet they must be distorted, to maintain the constancy of a velocity, as differently seen by observers in motion. Space contracts and time dilates whenever a body moves in relation to an observer (or—same thing, without an ether—whenever the observer moves in relation to the body). Motion through what? Motion through nothing. As long as one thing moves relative to another, space contracts and time dilates in the "other" reference frame.

You and I are standing in the same room, both of us wearing identical synchronized watches. I move towards you, and as I move, I observe your watch to run more slowly than my watch. And you observe my watch to run more slowly than your watch.

Notice how implausible this is. You are there, and I am here, and you are moving in relation to me. In consequence of that motion and *nothing else*, distances contract in your reference frame and time slows down.

The Einsteinians are well aware of this implausibility and so they reassure us. Don't be alarmed, they say. The time and length corrections are minuscule (as long as we are confined to everyday velocities). So the laity is urged go on thinking in the same old way. Our old clocks and rulers will still give us serviceable readings. The professionals on the inside know that everything has been remade, but the laity need not be disturbed.

So we are placated. We overlook the injury to common sense implicit in the theory. But many students of the theory still do find it difficult to sustain this mental acceptance, which I think is why few people ever feel that they really understand the theory of relativity. For it is the principle that matters, not the magnitude. Why, in principle, should we accept that any such a change in space or time really does occur?

It is important to realize that these adjustments to space and time are said to be real. They are not merely apparent. It's not like perspective, where receding objects *appear* to shrink. Lengths really do contract, in the Einsteinian scheme, and time really does slow down. An observer moving in relation to you really does see your time slowing down, and your space contracting (even though, within your own reference frame, you detect no such changes.)

It was a rearrangement of the physical world far more sweeping than anything that Lorentz or anyone else had in mind. When things move, in relation to one another, space and time are affected. And this applies across the board in physics, *not just to phenomena involving light*. In consequence of the special theory, all relative motion has to take into account the Lorentz transformations.

This is one of the least understood aspects of relativity. It is tempting to think that only electromagnetics are affected, because we start out by referring the moving observer to a beam of light. But all of physics is affected—mechanical laws as well as electromagnetic. It is not electromagnetic particles that contract because the observer moves relative to the light ray. It is space that contracts because Einstein has postulated that light rays approach all moving observers at the same speed.

Once we accept that *space* contracts whenever a reference frame moves in relation to an observer, then everything in that space will contract along with it. Contraction will shrink large objects like tables and chairs just as easily as electromagnetic particles.

The eminent British physicist Paul Dirac emphasized this point when he spoke at the Einstein centennial of 1979. He seemed mildly incredulous himself:

> In one respect, Einstein went far beyond Lorentz and Poincaré and the others, and that was in asserting that the Lorentz transformation would apply to the whole of physics and not merely to phenomena based on electrodynamics. Any other physical forces that may be introduced will have to conform to Lorentz transformations, which is going far beyond what the people who were working with electrodynamics were thinking about.[14]

A more controversial British physicist, Herbert Dingle, said the same thing. He taught relativity at Imperial College, London, and wrote a short book, *The Special Theory of Relativity* in 1940. He knew Einstein and for years accepted the theory without question. Two decades later, however, he concluded that it was "untenable." Then he disputed it in a second book *Science at the Crossroads*. In the earlier work, still accepting the orthodoxy, Dingle had written:

> This substitution [of length] must be made whenever length occurs, explicitly or implicitly, in a physical relation. And since every physical measurement that is made depends in part on the measurement of length, all physical measurements are thereby affected... The subject known as the Special Theory of Relativity is thus a revision of the basic principles of physics.[15]

The consequence of applying the Lorentz transformations to "the whole of physics" is that things don't quite add up any more. When a man runs inside a train in its direction of motion, we can no longer say that his speed relative to the ground is the addition of those two velocities. It is slightly less than that. Ten miles per hour plus another ten miles per hour don't quite add up to twenty. Yet the speed of light has not entered into it.

The science writer Isaac Asimov considered these matters and briefly wavered. "It seems strange and uncomfortable to accept so unusual a set of circumstances just to save Einstein's assumption of the measured constancy of the velocity of light," he said. In tracing these strange consequences to "Einstein's assumption," Asimov had it exactly right. But he quickly fell into line. "Nevertheless," he added. "whenever it has been possible to measure the velocity of light, that velocity has always been placed at one constant value..."[16]

Meanwhile, we may ask: What physical evidence supported relativity when the theory was proposed? Had anything comparably strange been observed in nature? I address this question in the next chapter. I believe the answer is that the only anomalous observation was our old friend, the Michelson-Morley experiment.

In later chapters I shall deal with more recent observations. Has time dilation, or space contraction actually been observed? It has been shown that *clocks* slow down as they move through the gravitational field, and that they speed up at a higher elevation. But no contraction of space has been observed in any experiment.

Notes Chapter 5

[1]   "On the Electrodynamics of Moving Bodies," John Stachel ed., *Einstein's Miraculous Year*, Princeton, 1998, p.124.

[2]   Stachel ed. p. 124.

[3]   Leo Sartori, *Understanding Relativity*, p. 48.

[4]   Banesh Hoffmann, *Albert Einstein: Creator and Rebel*, Viking Press, New York, p. 72.

[5]   Albert Einstein, "Reply to Comment by M. Abraham," August 1912, *Collected Papers*, Princeton, vol. 4, Doc. 8

[6]   Hoffmann, *Creator and Rebel*, p.75.

[7]   Hoffmann, *Relativity and its Roots,* p. 92.

[8]   Hoffmann, *Creator and Rebel*, pp.71-72.

[9]   Hoffmann, *Relativity and its Roots*, p. 92.

[10] Einstein's article appeared in *The Times* on Nov 28, 1919. Reprinted in Einstein, *Essays in Science*, Philosophical Library, 1934, pp.53-60.

[11] In 1907 Einstein published a more elaborate version of his special theory in a journal called *Jahrbuch der Radioaktivität und Electronik*. His description of the second postulate can be construed as saying that the speed of light is a constant, whatever the observer's motion. See Einstein's "*Jahrbuch*," (1907) *The Collected Papers of Albert Einstein*, vol. 2, Doc. 47, p.256. But his comment is still unclear. Einstein postulates that "the propagation velocity of every light ray in vacuum… becomes everywhere equal to a universal constant c…" This is to hold true "whatever the motion of the light source emitting the light ray or the motion of other bodies may be." What "does the motion of other bodies" refer to? The observer? Einstein then made it even more confusing. The principle of "the constancy of the velocity of light" is made plausible by "the confirmation of the Lorentz theory, which is based on the assumption of an ether that is absolutely at rest, through experiment." This must have confused everyone, for while Lorentz's theory indeed was based on "the assumption of an ether," Einstein's theory was based on the assumption that there is no ether.

[12] Albert Einstein, *The Special and the General Theory* (1917), p.17

[13] Ibid.

[14] P. A. M. Dirac, in *Some Strangeness in the Proportion; A centennial symposium*, ed. Harry Woolf, Addison-Wesley, 1980, pp.110-11.

[15] Herbert Dingle, *The Special Theory of Relativity*, Methuen, London, 1940, pp.8-9. Dingle, *Science at the Crossroads,* Martin Brian & O'Keefe (1972).

[16] Isaac Asimov, *Understanding Physics*, vol. 2, Dorset Press, 1966, p.104.

Chapter 6. Holton's Crusade

We see, then, that the special theory really was revolutionary. Those innocent-seeming postulates brought us to a strange place. The usual way of adding velocities no longer applied; universal time was to be replaced by multiple times, while others in motion relative to us had their own times, too; simultaneity between reference frames in motion could no longer be established.

What evidence in 1905 supported so disruptive a theory? Only one experiment seemed to require so great an upheaval. That was the Michelson-Morley experiment. Its unexpected result did imply that some basic conceptions in physics needed to be rethought.

There is much support for the view that Michelson-Morley was in fact the crucial precursor. One of relativity's earliest backers was Max Planck. According to Arthur I. Miller, Planck's support for relativity came even though he believed "the supporting data came only from the Michelson-Morley experiment."[1]

What evidence tended to support relativity when it was published? Not much, replied Caltech's Kip S. Thorne.

> Clocks of his era were too inaccurate to exhibit, at the low speeds available, any time dilation or disagreements about simultaneity, and measuring rods were too inaccurate to exhibit length contraction. The only relevant experiments were those few, such as Michelson and Morley's, which suggested that the speed of light on the Earth's surface might be the same in all directions. These were very skimpy data indeed on which to base such a radical revision of one's notion of space and time![2]

Yet, increasingly, we read that Einstein may not even have known about the Michelson-Morley experiment when he proposed his theory. We are certainly encouraged to believe that it played a minor role.

The man who has most vigorously pressed this interpretation is Gerald Holton, the Mallinckrodt Research Professor of Physics at Harvard, founder of the quarterly *Daedalus*, and a former editor of The Collected Papers of Albert Einstein. In recent decades he has been the most influential shaper of opinion about the origins of

Einstein's special theory.   His key articles on the topic were collected in his book *Thematic Origins of Scientific Thought.*[3]

For many years, the accepted interpretation was that Einstein was well familiar with Michelson-Morley before 1905. The primary evidence is Einstein's own comment, in his 1905 paper, about "the unsuccessful attempts to discover any motion of the earth relative to the 'light medium'." True, there had been a number of attempts. But the two by Michelson were by far the best known. Einstein surely was referring to Michelson-Morley, even if he didn't identify the experiment specifically. (The paper had no references of any kind.)

Today, nonetheless, Holton has succeeded in winning over many within the profession to a different position.

To gauge his success, we need only look at the article "History of Physics" in the *Encyclopedia of Physics*. At the end of the article we find a "see also" list of 29 additional topics. Among them is listed only one experiment: Michelson-Morley. But in the article on the history of physics, Lewis Pyenson writes: "There is strong evidence that, in 1905, Einstein was not aware of the Michelson-Morley experiments that had failed to detect the presence of ether drag relative to the earth's motion."[4]

Holton allowed that Michelson's experiment was "one of the most fascinating in the history of physics," and its "beauty and mystery" has been appreciated equally by "textbook writers and research physicists."[5]   But he concluded that the role of the experiment "in the genesis of Einstein's theory appears to have been so small and indirect that one may speculate that it would have made no difference to Einstein's work if the experiment had never been made at all."[6]

Why is this important? Einstein himself cited the Michelson-Morley result as *supporting evidence* for special relativity. But if the theory was in fact inspired by that experiment, it should not entirely surprise us to find that the experimental result is compatible with the theory.

In his popular account of relativity Einstein had asked: "To what extent is the special theory of relativity supported by experience?"[7]   He wrote that, at last, in his theory, Michelson's negative result—"a fact very perplexing to physicists"— was furnished with an explanation "incomparably more satisfactory" than anything earlier proposed by others.

Einstein, I submit, preferred to represent Michelson-Morley not as inspiration but as confirmation for his theory, precisely because in 1905 confirmation of the type that he needed was otherwise lacking. Holton recognizes this himself. He says at one point that Einstein

> ... accurately saw that the Michelson-Morley experiment could be used to gain credibility for the relativity theory in the community of physicists, and he wrote to Sommerfeld on January 14, 1908: "If the Michelson-Morley experiment had not placed us in greatest embarrassment, nobody would have perceived the relativity theory as (half) salvation."

Einstein later repeatedly made such references to the justificatory and pedagogic usefulness of the Michelson-Morley experiment.[8]

In looking for evidence supporting Einstein's theory, we do need something dramatic. Relativity distorted space and time. Holton always downplays the revolutionary character of relativity, arguing that Einstein instead sought continuity. Unconvincingly, he maintains that "the so-called revolution which Einstein is commonly said to have introduced into physics in 1905 turns out to be at bottom an effort to return to classical purity."[9] Holton, however, fails to show us just how revolutionary Einstein's theory was. Nor does he show how it restored classical purity.

James Bradley's discovery of stellar aberration (see chapter 10) had caused no upheavals. Fizeau's experiment on the speed of light in moving media (water) had no revolutionary implications. Nor did Michael Faraday's induction experiments, with which Einstein had opened his 1905 paper. In 1911, William F. Magie, the president of the American Physical Society, said that relativity was not essential to explain many experiments then under discussion, including Fizeau's. On the other hand "the negative result of the famous experiment of Michelson and Morley" did require an explanation.[10]

For over half a century, as Gerald Holton allowed, "historians of science as well as textbook writers were in almost unanimous agreement that the Michelson-Morley experiment was a crucial guide for Einstein in the genesis of his relativity theory." Both the physicists and the textbook writers were "virtually unanimous" on the point.[11] Among them was Max von Laue, a major supporter of Einstein and the author of the first textbook on relativity (published in 1911).

We know also that before 1905 Einstein was keenly interested in the attempts to detect an ether wind.   He even planned experiments of his own (although by inclination he was not an experimentalist).   In 1899, according to the second volume of his *Collected Papers*, Einstein "designed an experiment to test the effect of the motion of bodies relative to the ether on the propagation of light; in 1901 he designed a second such experiment, but was unable to carry out either."[12]

Einstein as Experimentalist

In one biography, we learn that from the time Einstein arrived at the Institute of Technology at Zurich, he "had the desire to conduct experiments on the Earth's movement against the ether." He did set up such an experiment in the lab, in mid-July, 1899.   But he "pushed the equipment beyond its limits and something gave," and as a consequence, "he seriously injured his right hand, which needed several stitches at the city clinic."[13]

Michelson himself was not in doubt.   In 1923, he told a reporter for the *Chicago Tribune* that "I think most people would say that [Michelson-Morley] was the experiment which started the Einstein theory of relativity.   That experiment is the basis of Einstein."[14] Likewise a book Einstein co-authored with Leopold Infeld discusses "the starting point of relativity theory." The only experiment mentioned in a fairly lengthy discussion is the "famous Michelson-Morley experiment."[15]

Robert A. Millikan, Michelson's colleague for many years at the University of Chicago and winner of the Nobel Prize in 1923 wrote:

> The special theory of relativity may be looked upon as starting essentially in a generalization from Michelson's experiment. . . [which had shown that there was] no observable velocity of the earth with respect to the aether.   That unreasonable, apparently inexplicable experimental fact was very bothersome to 19th century physics, and so for almost 20 years after this fact came to light physicists wandered in the wilderness in the disheartening effort to make it seem reasonable.   Then Einstein called out to us all, "Let us merely accept this as an established experimental fact and from there proceed to work out its inevitable consequences," . . . . Thus was born the special theory of relativity.[16]

Einstein's biographer Abraham Pais cannot resist an exclamation point when he writes that Einstein allowed that he had read Lorentz's paper of 1895, which discusses Michelson-Morley at length. Einstein had also read a paper published in 1898 by Wilhelm Wien, briefly describing experimental attempts to detect the motion of the earth through the ether. The Michelson-Morley experiment is among them.[17]

Einstein and Michelson met for the last time in Pasadena in 1931. Michelson, who was within weeks of his death, had already referred to relativity as a "monster" and had not stopped looking for new interpretations of the ether. Many eminent physicists were present, including Millikan, Hale and Hubble. After an elaborate dinner Einstein gave a short speech in which he addressed Michelson and the assembled company.

> It was you who led the physicists into new paths, and through your marvelous experimental labors prepared for the development of the theory of relativity. You uncovered a dangerous weakness in the ether theory of light, as it then existed, and stimulated the thoughts of H. A. Lorentz and Fitgerald from which the special theory of relativity emerged.[18]

But as the years went by, Einstein became more and more vague about his prior knowledge of the experiment. Increasingly, he gave the impression that the special theory had occurred to him as a result of pondering universal principles—his mind untrammeled by experimental minutiae. In 1942 he wrote to Bernard Jaffe: "I was pretty much convinced of the validity of the principle before I did know this experiment and its results." Michelson's result, he added, "showed that a profound change of the basic concepts of physics was inevitable."[19]

Does Not Remember if he Knew

In a 1953 letter to Michael Polanyi Einstein wrote: "In my own development Michelson's result has not had a considerable influence. I even do not remember if I knew of it at all when I wrote my first paper on the subject (1905)."[20]

Starting in 1950, R. S. Shankland, Professor of Physics at Case-Western Reserve, corresponded with Einstein on the role of Michelson-Morley. He had worked with Dayton Miller on some of the later versions of the experiment. Einstein at first said that only after 1905 had Michelson-Morley come to his attention. "Otherwise I would have mentioned it in my paper." The experimental results that had most influenced him were the observations on stellar aberration (first made by James Bradley), and Armand Fizeau's experiment of 1851. "They were enough," he said.[21]

Two years later, however, Shankland went to see Einstein and asked the same question. When did he first hear of Michelson-Morley?

"This is not so easy," Einstein replied. "I am not sure when I first heard of the Michelson experiment. I was not conscious that it had influenced me directly during the seven years that relativity had been my life. I guess I just took it for granted that it was true."

Then, in a later letter to Shankland, in December, 1952, Einstein said he learned of Michelson-Morley "through H. A. Lorentz's decisive investigations of the electrodynamics of moving bodies (1895), with which I was acquainted before developing the special theory of relativity."[22]

Abraham Pais seemed critical of Einstein about all this. He quotes Einstein's letter saying he didn't recall whether he knew of Michelson's experiment and comments: "Why this need not to remember, or, at best, to underplay this influence?"[23]

Pais also gives a firm answer to the questions: Did Einstein know of Michelson's work before 1905? Did it influence his creation of the special theory of relativity? "Yes, unquestionably," to both questions.[24]

John Stachel, the first editor of the Einstein Papers, thinks "there is strong indirect evidence that [Einstein] must have known of the Michelson-Morley experiment by 1899."[25]

Michelson pedagogically easier

In his own textbook, Holton proved to be more cautious than some of his followers. Describing the theory of relativity for those who have not already encountered it, he first reassured his readers that Einstein himself "did not rely on" Michelson-Morley. Nonetheless, it would be "pedagogically easier" for him to present that experiment as a prelude to any explanation of relativity.[26] He then describes the experiment as a logical precursor, much as the textbooks of old had done.

More recently, Holton seems to have been abandoned by his former graduate student, Arthur I. Miller, who published a study of the special theory in 1982. Then he revisited the question in his later book comparing Picasso and Einstein. He had earlier "systematically set up a classification of the books, monographs and journals Einstein had definitely read, very probably read," and so on. By the time he published his Picasso book (2001), Miller seemed adamant: "The objective historical fact is that Einstein had studied the Michelson-Morley experiment prior to 1905."[27]

In the end, perhaps it is not of crucial importance whether we view the famous experiment as confirmation or as inspiration for Einstein. But if it was the latter, it cannot easily do duty as the former. Reenlisting it as a confirming result is circular.

One thing is clear, as Holton showed in his own textbook. Debate over the origins of special relativity has made life harder than ever for authors of "easy Einstein" books. How was it that Einstein came up with so disruptive a theory if he was unaware of its comparably disruptive experimental precursor?

Those deferential to Holton's Crusade are sometimes forced into implausible or untenable accounts of the origins of relativity. Increasingly, for example, we are told that Einstein relied on his own intuition about the way the speed of light must behave. What, other than Michelson-Morley, obliged Einstein to propose so revolutionary a theory?

Notes: Chapter 6

[1]   Arthur I. Miller, *Albert Einstein's Special Theory*, p. 239, 341.
[2]   Kip Thorne, *Black Holes and Time Warps*, W.W. Norton, 1994, pp.78-9.
[3]   Gerald Holton, Thematic Origins, Chapters 6, 8.
[4]   Lewis Pyenson, "History of Physics," *Encyclopedia of Physics*, Addison- Wesley, 1981, p. 407
[5]   Holton, *Thematic Origins*, p.282; next sentence, Ibid, 478
[6]   Holton, *Thematic Origins*, p. 345.
[7]   Einstein, *Relativity, The Special and the General Theory*, p 49.
[8]   Holton, *Thematic Origins*, p. 479.
[9]   Holton, *Thematic Origins*, p. 195.
[10] William F. Magie, "The Primary Concepts of Physics," *Science*, Feb 23, 1912, p. 288.
[11] Holton, *Thematic Origins*, pp. 477-78; 288; 290.
[12] *Collected Papers of Albert Einstein*, v 2, 259. See his letter to Mileva Maric, 10 September 1899, and to Marcel Grossman, 6 Sept 1901.
[13] Michael White and John Gribbin, *Einstein: A Life in Science*, Plume, 1995, p. 40.
[14] Loyd Swenson, *Ethereal Aether*, pp. 203-4.
[15] Albert Einstein and Leopold Infeld, *Evolution of Physics*, 1938, p. 172, 183.
[16] R. A. Millikan, "Einstein on his 70th Birthday," *Rev. Modern Physics,* 1949, pp. 343-44.
[17] Abraham Pais, *'Subtle is the Lord': The Science and the Life of Albert Einstein,* Oxford Univ. Press, 1982, p. 118.
[18] Holton, *Thematic Origins*, p. 368.
[19] Bernard Jaffe, *Michelson and the Speed of Light*, Doubleday & Co., 1960, pp. 100-101.
[20] Holton, *Thematic Origins*, p. 340; 343.
[21] Einstein to Shankland, Holton, *Thematic Origins*, p. 300, 301.
[22] Einstein letter to Shankland, *Am. J. Physics*, 32 (1964), p. 16.
[23] Pais, *Subtle*, p. 172.
[24] Pais, *Subtle*, p. 116.
[25] John Stachel, "Einstein and Ether Drift Experiments," *Physics Today*, 40, 1987, p. 45.
[26] G. Holton and Steven Brush, *Introduction to Concepts and Theories in Physical Science, 2nd ed.* Princeton, 1985, p. 505.
[27] Arthur I. Miller, *Einstein, Picasso*, Basic Books, 2001, p. 184.

Chapter 7. On What Evidence?

Faraday's Law of Induction

The only anomalous result that Einstein mentioned in 1905 (other than the "unsuccessful attempts to discover any motion of the earth relative to the 'light medium'") was one that he put right at the beginning of his paper. It was well known that whether a wire conductor is moved in relation to a magnet, or a magnet is moved in relation to a wire, he wrote, the same electric current is induced in the wire. The observed phenomenon "depends only on the relative motion of the conductor and the magnet."

As the Einstein scholar John Stachel put it:

> the ether theory gives a different explanation for the origin of the current in the two cases. In the first case an electric current is supposed to be created in the ether by the motion of the magnet relative to it (Faraday's law of induction). In the second case, no such electric field is supposed to be present since the magnet is at rest in the ether, but the current results from the motion of the loop through the magnetic field (Lorentz force law). This asymmetry of explanation [is] not reflected in any difference in the phenomena observed...[1]

Despite its prominent place in Einstein's paper, books on relativity usually omit induction entirely in accounting for the origins of the theory. The symmetry of the induced current "had been known ever since Faraday first described the effect in 1831," as Gerald Holton wrote. "Few physicists, if any, can have thought in 1905 that there was something of fundamental importance in the asymmetry [of the explanation] to which Einstein pointed."[2]

Einstein later wrote that the current's indifference as to which is moved led him to postulate the first or "relativity principle." The main difficulty that still "had to be overcome was in the constancy of the velocity of light," he added. At first Einstein thought he "would have to give [this] up," but he found a way around his problem by *postulating* a constant light speed and then "relativizing the concepts of time and length."[3] Faraday's induction, known for decades, supported the first, or relativity postulate but was not something so earth-shaking as to oblige us to reconstruct space and time. That was deduced purely in consequence of Einstein's second, speed-of-light postulate.

Thought Experiments

In accounting for the origins of the theory, a famous thought experiment is cited more and more frequently. Einstein recalled, late in life, that at the age of 16 he hit upon a "paradox" within which "the germ of the special relativity theory is contained." If he were to pursue a beam of light with the velocity c, he speculated, he "should observe such a beam as a spatially oscillatory electromagnetic field at rest." But there "seems to be no such thing, whether on the basis of experience or according to Maxwell equations."

This he viewed as a paradox, and by then (he was writing in 1946), "everyone knows" that "all attempts to clarify it were condemned to failure." That failure persisted just as long as the "axiom of the absolute character of time, viz., of simultaneity, unrecognizedly was anchored in the unconscious." So he came to see the "arbitrary character" of this axiom, and that in turn led him to see "the solution of the problem."[4]

But such "experiments," in which impossibilities are imagined, cannot be treated as evidence.   Similarly, in this book I have disregarded Einstein's famous thought experiment about twins, in which one of the pair travels at high speed, turns around and returns younger than the stay-at-home twin. No such experiment has ever been done, and its imagined outcome entails acceleration which disqualifies it from the realm of special relativity anyway. A famous experiment with traveling atomic clocks *was* carried out, however, and this important experiment is discussed later.

In his "beam of light" paradox, Einstein was really saying nothing more than that imagining something impossible allowed him to conclude that a false axiom about time had been embedded in the unconscious mind. Therefore, that axiom was rejected.

In   contrast, illustrating   the indulgent trend of modern commentary, *Discover*'s Corey S. Powell, an adjunct professor at New York University, thinks that Einstein's thought experiments shows "the universal nature of his thinking." It enabled him to unearth "shortcomings in current physical theory," and respond to them by "inventing his own physics and finding new ways to measure space and time."[5] Creativity is to be admired, certainly, but not even Einstein can be permitted to invent his own physics.

Double Stars

A further piece of evidence is worth putting on the table, even though it wasn't available until several years after the special theory was published. But Einstein promptly incorporated it into his popular work, *Relativity: The Special and the General Theory* (1917), and it deserves to be considered.[6]

In 1913, the Dutch astronomer Willem de Sitter had analyzed the light coming from certain double stars, whose orbital plane is aligned so that, in the course of their mutual circling, one star is moving generally toward the Earth while the other is moving away. But if the light from these stars proceeded toward us at different speeds, one with the star's orbital velocity added to the speed of light, the other with its velocity subtracted, they would not appear to us as two distinct stars. We would see time-delayed images, sometimes resulting in *three* apparent stars, as the faster moving light from a star that has turned toward us in its orbit catches up with the earlier, slower light when the star was receding. But we never see that. They always appear as double stars.

Einstein drew attention to De Sitter's observation as a way of confirming his second postulate: the speed of light is unaffected by the motion of the light *source*. If by then the ether had remained in good standing among physicists, this claim might well have been considered unremarkable, because with a luminiferous medium, the light from both stars would have launched forth at the standard velocity of light in that medium. By 1913, moreover, the ether was still widely accepted, as Einstein's special theory had not yet transformed public opinion on the topic. Etherists would have no trouble believing that the speed of light from double stars *would* be unaffected by their motion.

De Sitter's claim was nonetheless important, because the wave theory of light was still contending with the emission theory of Walter Ritz (and others). Ritz claimed that light traveled in particle streams, as indeed Newton had thought. But double stars seriously weakened the emission theory. As the light source approached the Earth, the speed of particle stream should increase, just as bullets go faster if fired from a gun moving toward the target. De Sitter's evidence therefore strengthened the competing wave theory.

But as Einstein could see, with no further role for the ether — abolished by his special theory—the new double-star data showed that light, whether rays or particles, definitely did not approach at differing speeds from moving sources. Therefore it was true that De Sitter's analysis tended to support both the wave theory of light and Einstein's speed-of-light postulate.

In *Special Relativity*, A. P. French adds an interesting footnote. It has been more recently argued, he says (citing an article in the *American Journal of Physics*) that "since these binary star systems are usually surrounded by a gas cloud, which absorbs and then re-radiates the light from the stars, the speed of the light that crosses interstellar space may in any case be independent of any possible influence of the original moving sources."[7]

French's comment is of interest to the proponents of Petr Beckmann's theory—that the local gravitational field is the luminiferous medium—because in this theory, too, twin stars would tend to be enveloped in a blended gravitational field. It would absorb and re-radiate the light from the orbiting stars at a speed determined by their joint gravitational medium, not by the stars' separate motion. Therefore the binary star result is consistent with Beckmann's theory in addition to Einstein's.

Role of Maxwell Equations

Commentators today are ever more inclined to say that Einstein's speed of light postulate is implied by the Maxwell equations.[*] If so, however, one could also claim that the special theory itself is little more than a deduction from Maxwell's electromagnetic ideas.

The modern fashion is to put as much distance as possible between special relativity and Michelson-Morley, and then to attribute the second postulate to Maxwell's electrodynamics. In *My Einstein*, for example, Janna Levin, a professor of physics and

---

[*] The Maxwell equations are a set of four equations stating the properties of electrical and magnetic fields and relating them to charge and current. They are written in concise, unfamiliar notation and are not for amateurs or arts majors. Faraday's law of induction is one of those equations. Worked out by Maxwell in the 1860s, they were first put in mathematical form by Oliver Heaviside in 1884.

astronomy at Barnard College, says that Einstein "realized that space and time are relative." She continues:

> He came to this incredible conclusion through the idea that the speed of Maxwell's electromagnetic light is a fundamental constant. This simple assertion is actually outrageous. Our familiar experience is exactly contrary. For instance, if you race toward a moving train, its speed relative to you changes. But if you race toward a beam of light, its speed, as measured by you will, remarkably, always be c. ... The implications are surreal and Einstein worked them out in imaginative thought experiments.[8]

The idea that relativity theory flowed from Maxwell has also been adopted by John and Mary Gribbin. "Einstein had realized that no experiment involving Maxwell's equations could ever detect motion relative to this hypothetical absolute rest frame." His second postulate, in fact, "comes straight from Maxwell's equations."[9]

In the same vein, John Gribbin wrote in *Deep Simplicity* (2004):

> It is this requirement from Maxwell's equations that the speed of light is a constant for all observers, no matter how they are moving, that led Albert Einstein to develop the special theory of relativity in 1905.[10]

The most eminent recruit in support of the Maxwell-equation view is Stephen Hawking. In 2007, he contributed introductions to a volume of Einstein's scientific writings. In one commentary he wrote:

> ... . Einstein's 1905 special theory of relativity grew out of a simple observation. The theory of electromagnetism discovered by James Clerk Maxwell in the 1860s showed that whether we are moving toward or away from a beam of light, the light will always approach you at the same speed. This is not true of our experience in the everyday world.[11]

But it is not clear that Einstein ever did make such a claim, although he undoubtedly set such an interpretation in motion. In an unadorned footnote to his $E = mc^2$ paper, published later in 1905, he wrote: "The principle of the constancy of the velocity of light is of course contained in Maxwell's Equations."[12]

As it stands, however, this is ambiguous. Read one way, it is uncontroversial. Read another, it is problematic. The point is that Maxwell accepted the existence of the ether and assumed that light was propagated in the ether at a constant speed. It would be unaffected by any motion of the light *source* within that medium. By 1905, however, Einstein had rejected the ether. It is not clear whether Einstein in this paper assumes an ether or not.

But our more recent authors all accept that the ether is no more. Yet they insist that without an ether the speed of light is a constant *according to Maxwell*, no matter how the observer moves. That does correspond to Einstein's second postulate, but it is not something that can be deduced from the Maxwell equations. If it could be, Einstein would not have needed to postulate it in 1905.

Furthermore, Maxwell himself would have had no reason to believe that the Earth's motion through the ether could be detected. Yet he argued that a reflected light beam would have different speeds, coming and going, and his communications on this subject first inspired Michelson to carry out his experiment. If these recent interpretations of Maxwell were correct, his own equations should have told him that no such speed differentials were to be expected.

Not only did Maxwell assume that there was such a difference, he published an article claiming as much in the *Encyclopedia Britannica*. Maxwell wrote: "If it were possible to determine the velocity of light by observing the time it takes to travel between one station and another" on the earth's surface,

> we might by comparing the observed velocities in opposite directions, determine the velocity of the aether with respect to these terrestrial stations. All methods, however, by which it is practicable to determine the velocity of light from terrestrial experiments depend on the measurement of the time required for the double journey from one station to the other and back again, and the increase of this time on account of a relative velocity of the aether equal to that of the earth in its orbit would be only about one hundred millionth part of the whole time of transmission, and would therefore be quite insensible.[13]

Because he thought the difference would be too small to measure he proposed another method, this one yielding a potentially larger, "first order" effect; not depending on reflected light. It involved timing the eclipses of Jupiter's moon at different stages of its orbit, relative to the earth's position. Maxwell wrote a letter to D. P. Todd of the Nautical Almanac Office and the editor of *American Ephemeris* in Washington, about the possibility of confirming this experimentally.

Maxwell died soon after that, in November 1879. Recognizing the letter's importance, Todd sent it to *Nature*, which published it.[14]

It was about the last thing that Maxwell wrote. A. P. French is one of the few authors to have discussed it.[15] Maxwell's letter and encyclopedia article plainly undermine the claim that he believed, or that his equations predicted, that the speed of light would be the same in all reference frames.

Michelson saw Maxwell's letter and it inspired him to carry out his first experiment. He realized that the effect that Maxwell thought would be "quite insensible" was in fact "easily measurable" with his improved interferometer.[16] (But Maxwell's later suggestion, timing the eclipse of Jupiter's moons, really was not feasible.)

So the Michelson-Morley experiment was born. It is an irony, surely, when one delves into Maxwell's ideas about the ether and the speed of light, that instead of leading us away from Michelson's experiment, they lead us straight back to it. Far from rendering the Michelson-Morley experiment superfluous, as far as the origin of relativity is concerned, Maxwell's ideas actually gave rise to the famous experiment, historically.

The mistake made by recent commentators, surely, is to assume that in thinking about Maxwell's electrodynamics it is all the same whether the ether exists or not. If there is a medium, light speed is a constant with respect to that medium. If there is no medium, and either the light source or the observer moves, the speed of the approaching light beam will vary. If one then decides, for theoretical reasons, that the speed of light must be a constant, and one postulates it —"let's assume that the speed of light is a constant for all observers"—then space and time logically must be corrected so that they always produce, mathematically, the unvarying speed that has been postulated. That is the path that Einstein took.

In my view, then, the claim that Einstein's second postulate is implied by the Maxwell equations must be rejected. If it were true, we would be reduced to claiming that Maxwell didn't understand his own theories. This leaves us, as we began, with the Michelson-Morley experiment as the sole support for the theory of relativity at the time it was published.

Notes: Chapter 7

[1] John Stachel, *Einstein from 'B' to 'Z'*, Birkhauser, Boston, 2002, p. 162.

[2] Gerald Holton, *Thematic Origins*, p. 381, 383.

[3] John Stachel, *Einstein's Miraculous Year*, p. 111.

[4] P. A. Schilpp ed., in *Albert Einstein*, "Autobiographical Notes," 1949, p. 53.

[5] Corey Powell, *My Einstein*, Pantheon Books 2006, p. 101.

[6] Einstein, *Relativity: The Special and the General Theory*, p. 17.

[7] A. P. French, *Special Relativity*, W.W. Norton & Co., 1968, p. 74.

[8] Janna Levin, *My Einstein*, p. 183.

[9] John and Mary Gribbin, *Annus Mirabilis*, Chamberlain Bros, N.Y. 2005, p. 96.

[10] John Gribbin, *Deep Simplicity*, 2004, p. 20.

[11] *A Stubbornly Persistent Illusion: The Essential Scientific Works of Albert Einstein,* commentary by Stephen Hawking, Running Press Book Publishers, Phila. Pa., 2007, ix.

[12] Einstein et al, *The Principle of Relativity*, (1923), Dover, p. 69.

[13] Maxwell, "Ether," *Encyclopedia Britannica*, op. cit.

[14] *The Scientific Letters and Papers of James Clerk Maxwell,* vol.3 (2002) ed. P.M. Harman, Cambridge University Press 2002, item # 734. p.767. *Nature*, Jan 29, 1880.

[15] French, *Special Relativity,* p. 49.

[16] Michelson's paper, see Loyd Swenson, *Ethereal Aether*, pp. 249-50.

Chapter 8. Mystery of Mass

> Consider a spaceship passing overhead. According to Einstein's theory, as its speed increases its mass increases. It becomes greater and greater, until at the speed of light (in theory) it becomes infinite. Since this is impossible it implies that the speed of light is unattainable ... As the spaceship (as viewed from Earth) gets shorter, it physically becomes more massive. In fact, when it is one-tenth its original length, it is ten times as massive ... Of the three dramatic changes with speed, the change in mass is the easiest to observe experimentally. In fact, scientists observe it every day around the world in high energy accelerator labs. ... Again, we have to be careful. This change is only evident to the observer on Earth; the observer on the spaceship notices nothing out of the ordinary.[1]
>
> Barry Parker, *Einstein's Brainchild: Relativity Made Relatively Easy!*

We have already seen that special relativity reduces space and time, previously regarded as autonomous, to a state of dependency; waxing and waning depending on the speed with which the observer moves. Now—in the comment by Barry Parker above—we find that mass meets the same fate.

Einstein and Infeld wrote in *The Evolution of Physics*:

> We know from mechanics that every body resists a change in its motion; the greater the mass the stronger the resistance ... But in the relativity theory, we have something more. Not only does a body resist a change more strongly if the rest mass is greater, but also if its velocity is greater. Bodies with velocities approaching that of light would offer a very strong resistance to external forces. In classical mechanics the resistance of a given particle was something unchangeable, characterized by its mass alone.[2]

In this chapter, I shall explore what happens when masses are moved. Later I will turn to the experiments claiming that time slows down in moving reference frames. (The space ship "gets shorter," in theory and in drawings. But space contraction has not yet been observed experimentally.)

Prof. Parker was not misstating the doctrine of the relativists, however. Jeremy Bernstein, in his book *Einstein*, published decades earlier, wrote: "A moving electron, or any massive object, becomes more massive when it is in motion *with respect to an observer* than when it is at rest with respect to the same observer."[3] [My italics.]

This is bound to leave readers puzzled. Parker (deliberately) begs the question of what is "really" going on. The observer on the ground thinks that the mass of the spaceship has increased, but the observer on the spaceship sees nothing out of the ordinary. Which is it? That is not a meaningful question, say the Einsteinians. The mass is either increasing, or not, depending on your point of view. In fact, as Parker did not say but might have, from the point of view of the fast-moving spaceship, the mass of the Earth, rushing back in the opposite direction, will be seen to have increased by a factor of ten. But earth-dwellers will notice nothing unusual.

By the rules of relativity, remember, no reference frame is privileged. Symmetry must reign. It is always permissible to assume that the observer is located within the "other" inertial frame—that of the spaceship or the high-speed particle. And from these points of view the observer will see no change within his own environment.

In *The Nature of the Physical World*, Arthur Eddington takes us on this imaginary journey. He examines a fast-moving particle from its own point of view.

> It is an ordinary electron in no wise different from any other. But is it travelling with unusually high speed? 'No,' says the electron, 'that is your point of view. I contemplate with amazement your extraordinary speed of 100,000 miles a second with which you are passing me. I wonder what it feels like to move so quickly. However, it is no business of mine.'
>
> So the [electron] smugly thinking itself at rest, pays no attention to our goings on, and arranges itself with the usual mass and charge. It has just the standard mass of an electron, $9 \cdot 10^{-28}$ grams. But mass and radius are relative quantities, and in this case the frame to which they are referred is evidently the frame appropriate to an electron engaged in self contemplation, viz. the frame in which it is at rest.[4]

Eddington's intent was not to raise doubts about observer-based physics, nor about relativity, which he admired. Nonetheless, his account is bound to raise questions about a theory in which something as basic as mass depends on the observer's point of view.

At the least we may wonder whether Einstein's theory really did simplify physics.

When we talk about mass in this context, we are not talking about matter. It is a point repeatedly stressed by Ralph Baierlein, the author of *Newton to Einstein*. When describing what it is that changes with velocity, we are talking about an *attribute* of a thing, not the thing itself.[5] The *matter* of a particle has the same number of atoms whatever its speed. We are talking about an attribute, its inertia, or inertial mass. It is a measure of the reluctance of a given piece of matter to change its state of motion.

The increase of inertial mass with velocity is observed in particle accelerators, and we are told that this gives us the best confirmation of special relativity. Relativity indeed does provide an explanation of sorts. But there was all along a better one—one that does not oblige us to believe that if we travel alongside a fast-moving particle, its mass stays unchanged even as the mass of everything else outside it is observed to increase.

Mass Increase, Pre-relativity

The increase of inertial mass with velocity was observed before relativity existed and was satisfactorily accounted for. When Einstein's theory was published a few years later it was not regarded as a missing ingredient, essential if the then-recent discoveries about mass were to be understood.

These experiments on the increase of inertia could be done only with atomic particles because solid objects were far too massive to reach the necessary speeds. Gilbert Lewis of M.I.T. said in 1908 that a ton weight, given the velocity of the fastest cannon-ball, "would ... gain in mass by less than one millionth of a gram."[6]

The physicist Walter Kaufmann began experimenting on atomic particles in 1901. Accelerators did not yet exist, so he used electrons ejected from a naturally occurring radioactive material, radium. The mass of the ejected electrons appeared to increase along with their velocity. But the energy of these particles could only be guessed at, so the results were uncertain. Soon, however, experimenters showed that one of the most prized ideas in physics, the conservation of mass, was in doubt.

Henri Poincaré, an early analyst of these matters, was perhaps the leading physicist and mathematician of his day. In 1905, he published *The Value of Science* and when he wrote it Einstein's special theory had not yet been published. He thought the apparent increase in the inertia of moving particles challenged what he called "the principle of Lavoisier," or the conservation of mass.

The stakes were high. "Certainly this one is not to be touched without unsettling all mechanics," he wrote.[7]

Maybe this conservation law only "seems true to us" because "merely moderate velocities are considered." The conservation of mass might "cease to be true for bodies animated by velocities comparable to that of light."

Fast-moving particles can be deflected by a magnetic field, and by comparing these deflections, experimenters could measure both the velocity of the electrons and their inertial mass. Calculations by Abraham and Kaufman had definitely shown that physicists would have to "change the definition of mass," so that henceforth mass "augments with the velocity."

"Need I point out," Poincaré continued, with a hint of drama, "that the fall of Lavoisier's principle involves that of Newton's?"

He meant Newton's Second Law.

Newton, Mass and Fundamentals

Newton began his *Principia* with a discussion of mass, but his comments, some thought, were not satisfactory. He defined mass in terms of *quantitas materiae*, or quantity of matter, "arising from its density and bulk conjointly."[8] Two hundred years later, Ernst Mach pointed out the circularity. "As we can only define density as the mass of a unit of volume, the circle is manifest," he wrote.[9]

Eddington said of Newton's definition: "The experimenter was given no indication how he was to recognize the same 'quantity of matter' when presented in different forms, e.g. wool and lead... . Although it was not recognized at the time, no statement about mass (unless restricted to one kind of matter) was ever verified experimentally."[10]

Newton did distinguish between gravitational and inertial mass, and was the first to do so. An experimenter confronted with a cement ball and an identical-looking Styrofoam ball doesn't have to lift them to see which is which. He can push them sideways, or kick them. His stubbed toe will reveal the cement ball. Its reluctance to budge is a measure of its inertial mass.

Gravitational mass, on the other hand, can be measured by the elongation of a spring from which a weight is suspended. But that may vary with location. On a mountaintop it is less than at sea level, because, at elevation, the gravitational force is smaller. It is smaller because it is further from the center of the Earth.

We need these two forms of mass to account for the "remarkable property" of gravitational fields, as Einstein put it, that bodies under the influence of gravity accelerate at a rate that is independent of their material composition.[11] A lump of lead and a block of wood fall with the same acceleration, as was demonstrated (according to legend) at the Leaning Tower of Pisa. So gravitational and inertial mass are said to be equal in value.

The physicist Max Jammer wrote a treatise on mass, concluding that although it is fundamental to physics, it "is still shrouded in mystery."[12] For we never observe it directly. What we observe is the extension of a spring in gravitational mass; or a change in its position in inertial mass. By observing balls colliding and rebounding we can say that one mass is equal to another, but not what either really *is* in itself. That is why the notion of mass seems so basic. The same is true of time and space.

Newton's Second Law gives us the relationship between force, mass and acceleration, and it is historically important in our understanding of mass. $F = ma$ is perhaps the second best known equation in physics, and it's odd that both it and the best known (see the following chapter) involve mass, something that itself is said to be "shrouded in mystery."

An outside force acting on a stationary, balanced body will accelerate it, and what it tells us is that if this force is continuously, unceasingly applied—and we somehow get rid of the force of friction—the body will continue to accelerate without end, eventually exceeding the speed of light. Therefore Newton's second law is strictly speaking in conflict with the well known 20th century claim that nothing can exceed the speed of light.

But by the late 19th century experiments suggested that atomic particles don't really move as Newton had decreed. On the contrary, they react as though there is an upper limit to their speed. As they approach it, ever-increasing levels of force are required to increase their speed by a small amount.

Before Einstein, then, this discovery led to the general conclusion that mass, contrary to what everyone had earlier thought, wasn't "conserved" after all. It was something that depended on—increased with—velocity.

The new experiments with Cathode rays appeared to justify "the doubts of Lorentz concerning Newton's principle," Poincaré continued. And with momentous consequences: From these discoveries, if confirmed, there would arise "an entirely new mechanics." It would be "above all characterized by this fact, that no velocity could surpass that of light, any more than any temperature can fall below absolute zero."[13]

It's worth mentioning, because it is so widely believed that the idea of light speed as an upper limit was discovered by Einstein or was derived from his relativity theory. He certainly did enunciate and popularize that idea, but he didn't need relativity to do so.

Lest some be tempted to dismiss these pre-relativity interpretations as dissident physics, here is a comment from the entirely orthodox Leo Sartori:

> The possibility of a velocity-dependent mass had been discussed long before Einstein. Theories proposed by Lorentz and by Abraham had predicted that mass increases with velocity. An experiment performed by Walter Kaufmann in 1901 gave quantitative support to the idea. Kaufmann measured the deflection of beta rays (high speed electrons emitted in beta decay) by magnetic fields [and his experiments] suggested that the electron's mass does increase with velocity.[14]

Harvard's Gerald Holton adds further support. In his textbook, *Introduction to Concepts and Theories in Physical Science* (1985), he summarized the state of this particular art, pre-Einstein:

> It had been suggested before 1905 that the mass or inertia of an electron must increase with increasing speed, so that the acceleration, by a given force, of an already fast moving electron, would be less than that of the same electron when starting from rest. This mass increase had been found experimentally by W. Kaufmann (1902) and others, by deflecting in electric and magnetic fields the high speed electrons (β-rays) emitted by radioactive nuclei.[15]

Notice that the increase in the particle's inertia, or inertial mass, was inferred from its position. What was actually observed (then and now) was the deflection of particles in magnetic fields, at right angles to the velocity of the particle's velocity.

Charged particles can be made to curve to one side in a field, just as bullets fired horizontally will curve downward under the influence of gravity. This curving demonstrates an acceleration that is imposed upon the particles by the force in the magnetic field. But if the curvature of the observed path is less than expected, a "mass increase" is deduced. The particle's "reluctance" to move along a more tightly curved path is a measure of its inertia and therefore (at a given speed) of its mass.

Before Einstein, the observed increase in inertial mass was accounted for by Lorentz's electron theory. His theory, published in 1904, entailed radical departures from traditional dynamics. The masses of all particles were affected by their motion through the ether. The crucial difference between his and Einstein's theory was that Lorentz retained the ether and attributed the observed increase in inertial mass to real physical interactions as the electron traversed the ether field. Einstein attributed the increase in mass to the modification of space and time in moving reference frames.

In lectures at Columbia University in 1906, discussing the "question of electromagnetic mass," Lorentz used a hydrodynamic analogy that is still useful today. He noted that a large object moving through a fluid will encounter an ever-increasing resistance as the engine speed is increased. The idea here is the intuitive one that a medium more and more vigorously impedes the passage of a body, whether electron or submarine, as that body is pushed with increasing speed through that medium. The analogy can be carried only so far, however. Energy is irretrievably lost to the water as the submarine moves through it at any speed; whereas the total energy of the electron is entirely retrievable.

Lorentz never abandoned the idea of an all-pervasive medium. So his analogy is reasonable and the increase in inertia is clear. It depends for its magnitude on the speed with which the particle transits the medium. When Lorentz said at Columbia: "the electromagnetic mass is not a constant but increases with velocity," he was not thinking of motion considered abstractly, in relation to an observer, but of real physical interactions.[16]

Gilbert Lewis also demonstrated the increase of inertial mass with velocity—again without relativity. Retaining usual space and time, and the conventional laws of conservation, he derived the increased inertial mass of a moving body. Lorentz had already obtained the same equation, Lewis wrote, and now Lewis had done so using "strikingly different principles."

Lewis concluded that the inertial mass of a body is proportional to its energy content. "It is therefore necessary to replace that axiom of Newtonian mechanics according to which the mass of a body is independent of its velocity, by one which makes the mass increase with the kinetic energy."[17] All this was derived without relativity.

Recalling Lorentz's position of a century earlier, Max Jammer pointed out that one thing has been "completely ignored or at least thought to be negligible" in modern analysis—and that is the "interaction of a physical object" with its environment. He refers to that environment as the "medium" or "field." Even a vacuum is not empty space, he writes, and he seems to be flirting with restoring the ether. When a particle is acted on by a force, its acceleration "in the medium can be expected to be smaller than the hypothetical acceleration it would experience when moving in free space," he writes. If so, we can deduce "an increase in inertia owing to the interaction of the particle with the medium."[18]

Real Interactions

But for Einsteinians the medium has been abolished. So they are obliged to assume that in moving through empty space, the mass increases for no reason other than the relative motion of particle and observer. Mass increase, therefore, is derived by applying the space-contraction, time-dilation formulae—the Lorentz transformations—to the reference frame of the moving particle.

A real change in the particle's position is observed, in Einstein's theory as in any other. This change is predicted by relativity because the motion of the particle will alter space and time in its reference frame. Once these adjustments are entered mathematically, the new, actual location of the particle corresponds to its theoretical position.

All theories agree that when an observer (or a detector in a particle accelerator) sees a fast-moving particle, the inertia of that particle will be seen to increase. For the ether-based theories of Lorentz and Beckmann, that increase is caused by the mounting resistance that the particle encounters as it plows through the medium—the gravitational field in Beckmann's case—at higher speeds. Real physical interactions are involved.

For this reason, field-based theories and relativity theory only superficially make the same predictions. There is this difference:

In Einstein's theory, an observer (or instrument) moving with the swiftly moving particle would observe time to be *slowed down* in the reference frame of the particle accelerator or outside world. That is because either frame can be regarded as the moving one. Time dilation must be mutual and always observed in the "other" frame. Symmetry must prevail.

Ether-based theories, in contrast, give an asymmetrical result, and a more logical one. ("I see your clock running slower than mine. But you see my clock running faster than yours.") Clocks on the particle accelerator's walls, as observed by an instrument traveling along with the rapidly moving particle, would appear to be going *faster* than clocks accompanying the moving particles.

Which way does the evidence point? No observations have yet been made from the point of view of the fast-moving particles. The only experiment that approximates such a condition is that of atomic clocks carried around the globe (see chapter 16.) Mutual time dilation might convincingly demonstrate relativity theory, but it has not yet been observed.

The inertial mass of a particle moving through the ether or the gravitational field does increase, then. This was clearly understood before relativity theory was proposed. Einstein's theory gives the same result, but with the difference that the increase in inertial mass is not caused by physical interactions but is a consequence of the particle's motion relative to the observer.

The two approaches—with and without the ether—yield the same result because in all experiments that have ever been done, the vantage point from which observations are made is fixed on the surface of the Earth. Movement of the particle with respect to the observer is therefore not easily distinguished from its movement with respect to the ether—the local gravitational field. But observations from the point of view of the moving particle, which might confirm Einstein's theory, have not yet been made.

So inertial mass really may not be a "primitive" in physics after all—as indeed Einstein argued. But we may prefer to conclude from experiment and everyday logic that a particle's mass depends on its velocity with respect to the gravitational field; not with respect to the observer.

Notes Chapter 8

[1] Barry Parker, *Einstein's Brainchild:* Prometheus Books, 2000, pp. 60-61.

[2] Einstein and Infeld, *Evolution of Physics*, p. 205 .

[3] Jeremy Bernstein, *Einstein*, p. 94.

[4] Eddington, *The Nature of the Physical World*, 1928, p. 59-60.

[5] Baierlein, *Newton to Einstein: Trail of Light*, p. 238.

[6] Gilbert N. Lewis, "A Revision of the Fundamental Laws of Matter and Energy," *Philosophical Magazine* v. 16, Nov. 1908, p. 712.

[7] H. Poincaré, *The Value of Science*, The Science Press, 1907, pp. 103-04.

[8] Newton, see Max Jammer, *Concepts of Mass in Contemporary Physics and Philosophy*, Princeton, 2000, p. 3.

[9] Ernst Mach, *The Science of Mechanics*, Open Court, LaSalle, Ill. 1960, ch. 2 sect. 3.

[10] Arthur Eddington, *The Philosophy of Physical Science,* Macmillan, N.Y., 1939, p. 70.

[11] Einstein, *Relativity, the Special and the General*, p. 64.

[12] Jammer, op. cit., p. 167.

[13] Poincaré, op. cit. pp. 103-04.

[14] Sartori, *Understanding Relativity*, p. 212.

[15] Holton and Brush, *Introduction to Concepts and Theories,* p. 521.

[16] Pais, *'Subtle is the Lord'* ..., pp. 155-56.

[17] Gilbert N. Lewis, op. cit. p. 709, 714-17.

[18] Jammer, op. cit., p. 32.

Chapter 9. $E = mc^2$

Einstein's first derivation of the famous equation did use relativity, but later derivations showed that it was not necessary. Einstein himself published an "elementary derivation" without relativity in 1946.[1] Gilbert N. Lewis of M.I.T. derived it, also without relativity, in 1908.[2] Ralph Baierlein, who taught at Wesleyan, gives another derivation in his book *Newton to Einstein*. It makes "no use of Lorentz transformations or other results from the special theory of relativity."[3]

A century ago, Lewis said the equation "has also been obtained by Einstein, who derived it from the general equations of the electromagnetic theory with the aid of the so-called principle of relativity. That a different method of investigation leads to the same simple equation we have deduced, speaks decidedly for the truth of our fundamental postulate."

Einstein obtained the equation "as an approximate formula," Lewis added, while he had obtained it exactly. Lewis thought Einstein's derivation was approximate because he allowed that he was "neglecting magnitudes of the fourth and higher order," that is, very small magnitudes.[4]

Since the argument of this book is that experimental results given by relativity can also be derived without it, perhaps I could move on to the next chapter. To double check, however, I contacted the prominent Einstein scholar John Stachel, the first editor of the Einstein Papers and director of the Center of Einstein Studies at Boston University.

Very few laymen seemed to know about the alternative derivation of the famous equation, I said in an email. Did he agree? And did he accept that the alternative derivation was correct?

"Yes, I do agree on both counts," he replied.[5]

As to the claim by Gilbert Lewis (and later by Edmund Whittaker) that Einstein's derivation was "approximate," Stachel replied that he and a co-author had published an article in the *American Journal of Physics* arguing that such criticisms are "unwarranted."[6]

Despite the equation's prominence, it is not easy to find acknowledgments that it can be reached without relativity. It is not in the books about Einstein's life by Philipp Frank (1947), Ronald Clark (1971), Banesh Hoffmann (1972, Jeremy Bernstein (1973), Michael White and John Gribbin (1993), Denis Brian (1995), Albrecht Folsing (1997) and Walter Isaacson (2007). It is not in Harald Fritzch's *An Equation that Changed the World*; nor in David Bodanis's $E = mc^2$: *A Biography of the World's Most Famous Equation*. As far as I know the popular author and MIT professor Alan Lightman has not mentioned it. The popularizations of relativity by Lincoln Barnett, Martin Gardner, and Barry Parker also omit the "elementary" version.

Abraham Pais's *'Subtle is the Lord'* ... (1982) does discuss it,[7] as does Leo Sartori's *Understanding Relativity* (1996).[8] Max Jammer devotes a dozen pages to the topic in his *Concepts of Mass in Contemporary Physics and Philosophy* (2000).[9]

Books on Einstein avoid the error of saying that the equation *depends* on special relativity. They use vaguer language ("was derived from" is common). Clifford Will's *Was Einstein Right?*, for example, includes an appendix, "Special Relativity: Beyond a Shadow of a Doubt." It begins:

> It is difficult to imagine life without special relativity. Just think of all the phenomena or features of our world in which special relativity plays a role.
> Atomic energy, both the explosive and the controlled kind. The famous equation $E = mc^2$ tells how mass can be converted into extraordinary amounts of energy.[10]

Some of these authors presumably do know about the non-relativistic derivation. Perhaps their intention is to convince the world that the theory of relativity was momentous in its consequences.

In a recent paper, published by the *American Journal of Physics*, Baierlein takes Einstein himself to task for sometimes misrepresenting the relationship between mass and energy.[11] Contrary to the general belief, Baierlein wrote, the famous equation neither claims that mass is "converted" into energy no does it say that mass is "equivalent" to energy.

What Is Energy?

Before examining the mass-energy relationship more closely, however, the idea of energy itself deserves a brief review.

Energy was a latecomer to the field of physics. It is not something primitive, like space, time or mass. The concept of energy is not to be found in Galileo or Newton. Not until the 19th century is it formally introduced into physics. The notion that there is something identified as energy that is "conserved" throughout various physical changes was understood as a "law" only in the 1840s. Energy was adopted by physicists primarily because it was useful. The formula that defines the kinetic energy of an object in terms of its mass and velocity, for example, tells us how high the object will rise if it is thrown vertically against gravity.

The kinetic energy of a body— the energy derived from its motion—is proportional to the body's mass times the square of its velocity. The formula ($KE = \frac{1}{2} mv^2$) has a familiar look, especially if we substitute c for v. It is based on the premise that a force applied over a certain distance expends a certain amount of energy, the force being proportional to the body's mass times its acceleration. The fraction $\frac{1}{2}$ is needed because the work done in accelerating the particle is represented by the area of a triangle in a certain graph.

The relationship between kinetic energy, mass and velocity was established only recently, as the history of physics goes. G. Burniston Brown of University College, London, whose book *Retarded Action at a Distance* was admired by Petr Beckmann as an "alternative to the Einstein theory" preceding his own, summarized the little known story in the following remarkable paragraphs.

> In the early struggles to lay the foundations of dynamics, round about the time of Newton, the great argument was whether mv or mv^2 was the more suitable measure of the extra 'force' that a body could exert due to its motion. Newton defined the vague term 'momentum' clearly as 'the measure of it' by the product of the mass of the body and the measure of its velocity. Thomas Young thought that the product mv^2 should have a precise name, too, as it is of importance in calculations such as those finding the height to which a body rises when thrown upwards. He suggested energy.
>
> The term kinetic energy first appeared in an article in *Good Words* (a magazine edited at one time by Dickens), by Kelvin and Tait, and the product mv^2 (having acquired the half), became $\frac{1}{2}mv^2$.

> Potential was a mathematical function invented by Lagrange to make gravitational calculations easier. Rankine added the word 'energy' in 1853. It was thus transformed (by word magic) from a mathematical function into something which a physical body was said to 'have'.[12]

Conservation of energy claimed that energy is never lost but only transformed from one form into another. At the end of a pendulum's swing, the energy of its motion is converted into the energy of position (potential energy). But friction will gradually bring the pendulum to a halt. Has the energy then been lost? No, it has been converted again, this time into heat. Here the key experiments were done in the 1840s by James Prescott Joule, the son of a brewer in Manchester, England.

Brewers need accurate thermometers, and Joule (who inherited a fortune but was more interested in physics than in beer-making) was able to show that a plunging weight, which turned a paddle in water, warmed up the water by a fraction of a degree. The increased temperature replaced the energy dissipated by the falling weight. Joule must have dismayed his bride when he tried to show—on his honeymoon—that the water at the foot of a waterfall is warmer than it is at the top. It is, but not even a brewer's thermometer could detect so small a difference at the time.

The German physician Julius Robert Mayer had proposed that "force, once in existence cannot be annihilated, it can only change its form." (He used the German word *Kraft*, which today is sometimes translated as energy.) Von Helmholtz later summarized the contributions of Mayer and Joule in a paper published in 1847, "On the Conservation of Force [Kraft]." The term energy was introduced a few years later by the Scottish engineer William Rankine.[13]

Mayer asked: What other forms is energy capable of assuming? The answer came from Einstein. Bodies don't have to fall under the influence of gravity, move forward or gain or lose heat, to manifest their energy. It seems natural, he wrote, "to consider any inertial mass as a reserve of energy," whether it is moving or stationary.

What gave him reason for thinking that? Sometimes a part of the mass decays, and when that happens it is "accompanied by the release of enormous amounts of energy."[14]

By the late 19th century there were reasons for thinking of a lump of matter as a compact hoard of energy. But if it were true that "every gram of material contains this tremendous energy," why had it gone unnoticed for so long? Einstein likened matter to a miser. "It is as though a man who is fabulously rich should never spend or give away a cent," he wrote. "No one could tell how rich he was."[15]

Some elements of matter disintegrate on their own, discharging energy in the process. They are said to be radioactive. In 1896 Henri Becquerel discovered that uranium emitted such radiation. Placed in a darkened drawer, the metal left an image on the paper wrapping it; by 1898 Madame Curie and her husband had discovered polonium and radium, and they had the same properties.

When Ernest Rutherford went to Paris to investigate, in 1903, he saw that Pierre Curie's hands were "in a very inflamed and painful state due to exposure to radium rays." The Curies concluded that the radiation consisted of particles emitted with high energy content. When they gave Rutherford a radium sample to study he took it home in his waistcoat pocket.[16]

Radium did not *measurably* decrease in mass as it discharged energy, but as Einstein wrote in 1907: "It is possible that radioactive processes will be detected in which a significantly higher percentage of the mass of the original atom will be converted into the energy of a variety of radiations than in the case for radium."[17]

In 1905 Einstein wrote to his friend Conrad Habicht noting that "the principle of relativity, in conjunction with the Maxwell equations, requires that mass be a direct measure of the energy contained in a body; light carries mass with it. A noticeable decrease of mass should occur in the case of radium."[18] So the recently discovered phenomenon of radioactivity had given Einstein an important clue.

Lewis's Derivation

Gilbert Lewis's 1908 derivation, "A Revision of the Fundamental Laws of Matter and Energy," owed something to Friedrich Hasenohrl, an Austrian physicist killed on the front lines in World War I, who had shown that the kinetic energy of a "black body" cavity increased when bombarded with radiation. The mass of the system appeared to increase, and he produced a mass-energy equation close to Einstein's. His paper, concluding that $E = \frac{3}{4}mc^2$ was published in *Annalen der Physik*, about six months before Einstein's.[19] A black body placed in a beam of light, Lewis wrote, is subject to a pressure which moves it in the direction of the light beam. Such a body will acquire momentum, and (given the conservation of momentum) some other body must have lost equal momentum. Therefore the beam of radiation carries not only energy but momentum with it.

So, "knowing only that light moves with a certain velocity and that in a beam of light momentum and energy are being carried with this same velocity," Lewis wrote, we conclude that "something possessing mass moves with the velocity of light and therefore has momentum and energy."[20]

Like Einstein, Lewis concluded that "the mass of a body depends upon its energy content," and it is therefore necessary "to replace that axiom of the Newtonian mechanics according to which the mass of a body is independent of its velocity by one which makes the mass increase with the kinetic energy."

Baierlein's Objection

Ralph Baierlein objects to too close an identification of mass and energy, even from Einstein's pen. Almost every book on relativity claims that the famous equation describes "the *equivalence* of mass and energy," Baierlein wrote, and Einstein himself used the phrase. Diplomatically, he added: "I think it fair to say that, for Einstein in 1907, the 'equivalence of mass and energy' meant a numerical proportionality between the two quantities."[21]

Einstein's 1946 article even has "the equivalence of mass and energy" in its title. Petr Beckmann leveled the same criticism against this usage. The supposed "equivalence of mass and energy" is a "dimensional absurdity," he wrote.[22]

Mass is not "converted" into energy, either. They are better thought of as attributes that increase or decrease in proportion. For a given body, Baierlein wrote, "if one attribute increases, so does the other. The changes are concomitant and in the same sense."[23]

So the mass-energy relationship is quite unlike that between kinetic and potential energy, in which one really is "converted" into the other. In fact, it's almost the opposite. Inertial mass and energy rise and fall together.

Baierlein made his initial criticism in 1989. He also warned that "If you cannot substitute the word inertia for the word 'mass' in your sentence, then you are misusing the word 'mass'," Matter, on the other hand, "is palpable stuff; it is a thing. 'Mass' means inertia, a reluctance to undergo a change in velocity; it is an attribute (of a physical system)."[24]

> An attribute cannot be converted into a thing, and so energy cannot be converted into matter. Likewise, a thing cannot be converted into an attribute, and so matter cannot be converted into energy.[25]

Baierlein also recommended that we distinguish conversions from parallel changes.

> Changes in mass and energy occur in parallel, as Einstein pointed out in his first paper [the title of which was "Does the inertia of a body depend on its energy content?"] There is no conversion of one to another.

For eight years Baierlein taught a course at Wesleyan for non-scientists, prompting him to go back to basics. Eventually he collected his lectures into *Newton to Einstein*. He learned the simpler derivation of Einstein's equation from Eric Rogers. A graduate student at Princeton in 1961-62, Baierlein helped Rogers teach his course, which attracted non-scientists, just as Baierlein's would later. Rogers was Einstein's next-door neighbor, so perhaps it was from Einstein himself that he learned about the elementary derivation of the famous equation.

$E=mc^2$ and Nuclear Fission

In 1943, Robert Serber delivered five lectures to scientists gathered at Los Alamos lab, then still secret. He summarized what was then known about the building of an atomic bomb, and his expanded notes were published as *The Los Alamos Primer* in 1992.

"The popular notion took hold long ago that Einstein's theory of relativity, in particular his famous equation $E = mc^2$, plays some essential role in the theory of fission," Serber wrote. Einstein did alert the U.S. government to the possibility of building an atomic bomb, but relativity "is not required in discussing fission."[26]

We might with equal justice blame Newton's laws of motion for the invention of intercontinental ballistic missiles, Stanley Goldberg wrote.[27] George Gamow said that the mass-energy relationship was no more the basis for the invention of the atom bomb than it was for Nobel's discovery of nitroglycerine or for Watt's invention of the steam engine.

"Einstein's role in atomic bomb development was not the formulation of the $E = mc^2$ law," Gamow added, but a letter he wrote to President Roosevelt saying that a bomb was possible.[27]

A related misconception is that Einstein became the father of the atom bomb by foreseeing the energy released in a nuclear explosion and publishing the formula that "reveals" it.

Ralph Baierlein said how misleading this is. "Originally in the uranium nucleus there are a lot of protons all squeezed together," he told me. A wandering neutron is absorbed and then "splits" the nucleus. After that division those protons are farther apart, "because some of them are now in a barium fragment, some of them are in a krypton fragment and so on."

The explosive force comes mostly from "the reduction in electrical potential energy that shows up as kinetic energy. What really drives it is the electrical repulsion of the protons."[28]   The original atomic nucleus is like a compressed spring. When it is "sprung," it unleashes a lot of energy.

So here we really do see one form of energy (potential) converted into another (kinetic). We also see why it is appropriate to think of the atoms of matter as hoarding a lot of compacted "potential" energy. But the mass-energy equation was not dependent on relativity theory nor did it entail the invention of the atomic bomb.

Notes: Chapter 9

[1] Albert Einstein, *Out of My Later Years*, Philosophical Library, 1950, pp. 116-119.

[2] Gilbert N. Lewis, op. cit., pp. 705-717.

[3] Ralph Baierlein, *Newton to Einstein,* ch. 11 and appendix C.

[4] John Stachel, ed. *Einstein's Miraculous Year*, p. 164.

[5] John Stachel, e-mail to author, Dec. 2002.

[6] John Stachel, *Einstein: From 'B' to 'Z',* Boston, Birkhauser, 2002, p. 215.

[7] Abraham Pais, *'Subtle is the Lord'...* p. 148.

[8] Sartori, *Understanding Relativity*, p. 205.

[9] Jammer, *Concepts of Mass* (revised ed.) Princeton, 2000, chapter 3.

[10] Clifford Will, *Was Einstein Right*? Basic Books, N.Y. 1986, p. 245

[11] Baierlein, *Am. J. Physics*, April, 2007, p. 320.

[12] G. Burniston Brown, *Retarded Action at a Distance*, Cortney Publications, 1982, p. 19.

[13] Tony Hey and Patrick Walters, *Einstein's Mirror*, Cambridge, 1997, pp. 92-94.

[14] *Collected Papers of Albert Einstein*, vol, 2 "Jahrbuch," p. 287.

[15] Einstein, *Out of My Later Years*, pp. 51-52.

[16] Hey and Walters, *Einstein's Mirror*, pp. 114-118.

[17] Einstein *Collected Papers*, v.2 "Jahrbuch," English translation p. 288.

[18] Stachel, ed. *Einstein's Miraculous Year*, p. 5.

[19] Pais, *Subtle*, p. 148.

[20] Gilbert N Lewis, op. cit.,. p. 707.

[21] Ralph Baierlein, *Am. J. Physics*, April 2007, p. 321.

[22] Petr Beckmann, *Einstein Plus Two*, p. 64.

[23] Baierlein, *Am. J. Physics*, April, 2007, p. 320.

[24] Baierlein, "Teaching $E = mc^2$," *Am. J. Physics,* May 1989, p. 391.

[25] Baierlein, *Newton to Einstein*, p. 323.

[26] Robert Serber, *The Los Alamos Primer, The First Lectures on How to Build an Atomic Bomb*, introduction by Richard Rhodes, University of California. 1992, p. 7.

[27] Goldberg, *Understanding*, p. 156; Gamow, *Biography of Physics*, 1961, p. 188.

[28] Author's interview with Ralph Baierlein, May 2004.

Chapter 10. Stellar Aberration

Stellar aberration, known since the 18th century, is something that relativity or any other physical theory must accommodate. Aberration generally is a change in the apparent direction from which particles, wave-fronts or points of light approach an observer, in consequence of the observer's motion. We could be talking about raindrops, wind or light from a distant star. Bicyclists with a wind blowing across the road when they are stationary will feel a more frontal wind when they start bicycling. A driver at a stop light may see rain falling vertically, but at 50 miles an hour it will descend at an oblique angle. In the rain, people will tilt their umbrellas forward once they start walking if they want to stay dry. The raindrops are now (to the walker) "aberrated." The degree of aberration depends on the relative velocities of the walker and the falling rain.

So aberration qualifies as a relativistic phenomenon. Its apparent magnitude depends on the observer's motion. The same is true of the Doppler Effect. By the roadside, the siren of an approaching ambulance will suddenly drop in pitch as it passes you. To the driver, however, it will remain unchanged. It is an effect that depends on the motion of both the source and of the observer with respect to the medium.

The aberration of starlight was discovered in 1725 by an English astronomer, James Bradley. The professor of astronomy at Oxford, he was said to be "a good Newtonian both in method and in theory."[1] In order to observe a particular star, he found that he had to aim his telescope slightly ahead of the star's expected direction. The man walking in the rain inclines his umbrella forward in the same way.

A Journeying Thing

Bradley had found stellar aberration, but, as is so often the case, he had been looking for something else—stellar parallax. This is a change in the position of the stars, relative to one another, as a result of the Earth's changing position in its orbit. As I believe that the search for parallax has its modern analogy in the story of relativity, I shall return to it at the end of the book.

Bradley had chosen a star in the constellation of the Dragon that passed directly over his house at a particular time of year. He studied its location, both in relation to the zenith and in relation to the position of other stars at other times of the year. When it was overhead, he found, it was not quite in the expected place. But it was not parallax that he was seeing, because parallax would be a small side-to-side displacement. What Bradley observed was always a displacement in the direction of Earth's motion.

When he studied the positions of other stars, he found that in the course of a year they all showed the same angular displacement, depending only on their direction relative to the Earth's orbit. In a year, all stars appear to move around in tiny ellipses relative to a given compass point, with a maximum angle of aberration of 20 seconds of arc. The discovery of stellar aberration was a great achievement for it confirmed, as Banesh Hoffmann wrote, that "light is a journeying thing."[2]

It is said that Bradley found the correct explanation while crossing the River Thames on a boat. Observing the combined action of the moving boat and the wind on the boat's flag, it occurred to him that the unexpected direction of the star was a product of the combined movements of the Earth's orbital motion and of the light beam from the star. In an article published by the *Transactions of the Royal Society* in 1729, Bradley wrote:

> If light be propagated in time (which I presume will be readily allowed by most of the philosophers of this age) then it is evident from the foregoing considerations, that there will be always a difference between the real and visible place of an object, unless the eye is moving either directly towards or from the object.[3]

Since the Earth's orbital velocity was a known quantity, and the degree of aberration had now been observed with some accuracy, the speed of light could be calculated by trigonometry. Arriving at a speed of light more accurate than any previous estimate, Bradley was rewarded when he succeeded Edmond Halley as Astronomer Royal in 1742. So now astronomers knew not just that light was a journeying thing, but the speed at which it journeyed.

Aberration was at first understood in terms of the particle theory of light, which was then the dominant theory. Newton had embraced it and most of his contemporaries followed suit. It wasn't until the 19th century that the wave theory gradually supplanted the particle theory.

Breeze through the Trees

By 1804 Thomas Young had accepted that light was a wave, and he and Augustin Fresnel became the leading authorities on the new wave theory. Waves require a medium, and within a short time the ether's existence was considered to be as well established as the wave theory itself. Young then made a connection between stellar aberration and the ether with an image that stayed in people's minds throughout the 19th century.

"Upon considering the phenomena of the aberration of the stars," he wrote, "I am disposed to believe that the luminiferous ether pervades the substance of all material bodies, with little or no resistance, as freely, perhaps, as the wind passes through a grove of trees."[4]

The underlying idea came to dominate thinking about interaction with the ether. The ether was present, but did not impede the Earth's motion at all. Therefore we should not expect the ether to be entrained by the orbiting Earth.

At the same time, with the Earth orbiting the sun at about 40,000 miles per hour you couldn't entirely dismiss the possibility that the Earth really might sweep the luminiferous medium along with it; or do so partially. And if the ether *was* entrained, the Michelson-Morley result would be accounted for. Perhaps Michelson had been unable to find an "ether wind" because the ether at the Earth's surface was being pulled along by the Earth.

If so, however, starlight should show no aberration. How could it, absent relative motion between the ether and the telescope? That couldn't easily be dismissed either. Stellar aberration seemed to require an ether that was not entrained; Michelson's result seemed to require an ether that *was* entrained. You could have stellar aberration, or you could have an entrained ether. But it wasn't clear that you could have both.

Michelson captured the quandary back in 1881, when he wrote from Heidelberg to Alexander Graham Bell. Notice the way Michelson interpreted his failure to show a fringe shift:

"The experiments concerning the relative motion of the earth with respect to the ether have just been brought to a successful termination," he wrote, adding after a few sentences: "Thus the question is solved in the negative, showing that the ether in the vicinity of the earth is moving with the earth; a result in direct variance with the generally received theory of aberration."[5]

Since then, however, relativity theorists have been disposed to ignore Michelson's interpretation, and to assume that aberration is the determining factor: It precludes an entrained ether. Therefore any entrained-ether temptations we may have must be resisted. Stellar aberration has ever since remained as a textbook warning to dissidents and ether-sentimentalists: don't even think about escaping from Michelson's result by seeking refuge in an ether that is swept along by the Earth.

"The fact that the earth moves through the ether without affecting it is known by the aberration of starlight," Einstein's early biographer Philipp Frank wrote.   "Thus the phenomenon of aberration shows that the ether is not influenced by the motion of the earth."[6]   Gerald Holton: "The idea that the ether is substantially carried along by the earth was in direct conflict with the well established results of aberration experiments." [7]   If the ether "near the earth were carried along with it, the aberration would not take place," wrote A. P. French.[8]   Leo Sartori agreed: "ether-drag theory" left stellar aberration unexplained.[9]

Einstein's biographer Ronald W. Clark summarized it this way. Michelson-Morley seemed to leave us with only three possibilities:

> The first was that the earth was standing still, which meant scuttling the whole Copernican theory and was unthinkable. The second was that the ether was carried along by the earth in its passage through space, a possibility which had already been ruled out to the satisfaction of the scientific community by a number of experiments, notably those of the English astronomer James Bradley. The third solution was that the ether simply did not exist, which to many nineteenth century scientists was equivalent to scrapping current views of light, electricity and magnetism, and starting again.[10]

But there was a fourth possibility—that the ether was entrained at ground level but not entrained at a greater altitude,

The idea that the ether near the earth was partially entrained had earlier enjoyed some support. In 1845, long before Michelson, George Stokes of Cambridge suggested that "the earth and planets carry a portion of the ether along with them, so that close to their surfaces the ether is at rest . . ." Therefore, he thought, aberration could be explained "without the startling assumption that the earth in its motion around the sun offers no resistance to the ether."[11]

Stokes's dissent gave encouragement to the later Michelson. In a new paper, "The Relative Motion of the Earth and the Ether," he theorized that the entrainment might be reduced at a greater height. A fringe shift might therefore be detected by comparing light paths separated by a vertical distance.   Michelson tested this in 1897. Light rays were sent in opposing directions along the full 200-foot length of the Ryerson Laboratory building at the University of Chicago, then up 50 feet to an upper floor, along the upper level and then down again, finally completing a large rectangle.   But once again no fringe shift was found.   If there was one, it was "certainly less than a twentieth of a fringe," Michelson wrote.[12]

It followed from this latest result that "the earth's influence upon the ether extended to a distance of the order of the earth's diameter," he wrote.   Maybe as much as 8000 miles, in other words. But this struck him as "so improbable" that he once again rethought the issue.   A quite different interpretation seems to have occurred to him.

Michelson's underlying thoughts about the ether and its entrainment were not clearly expressed, either here or (as far as I know) anywhere else.   In fact, the development of his thinking on this crucial subject has never been fully clarified.   But he gave a clue to his new thinking in an article in the *Philosophical Magazine,* published in 1904.[13]   The theory of relativity was almost upon us.

Michelson was only tentative even then, and, as always, terse. He merely suggested by his new experimental design another way of looking at the matter.   Clearly the ether was being carried along by the Earth's orbital motion.   But was it also entrained by the Earth's *rotation*?   Possibly not.   That is what his new experiment would test.

Twenty years passed before the experiment was carried out.   It became known as the Michelson-Gale experiment and it did show a fringe shift.   The Earth's rotation had indeed been the key.   (See Chapter 14.)

Of course, if the ether simply is the local gravitational field as Petr Beckmann argues, then it certainly is carried along with the Earth; and it is also likely that the Earth rotates "within" its gravitational field.   And contrary to what Michelson had thought in

1897, it isn't at all improbable to think of this field as extending thousands of miles into space.   Plainly it does extend as far as the moon, a quarter of a million miles away, for the moon is held in its orbit by the Earth's gravitational field.

At this point we see that Michelson's thinking was coming close to what would eventually become Beckmann's theory.   And that is not entirely surprising either, for Beckmann arrived at his theory, in Prague, after studying the Michelson-Gale experiment.

Transitional Zone

One big question obviously remains: how can Beckmann's theory account for stellar aberration?

His answer is that there is a transitional region where the dominant gravitational field ceases to be that of the Earth and becomes that of the Sun. The transitional zone can be visualized as a "sharp boundary," as Beckmann wrote, rather than a "gradual transition."[14] We can think of the boundary as the surface of a bubble that surrounds or encloses the Earth's gravitational field and continually moves through the Sun's field—at the Earth's orbital velocity.

Meanwhile, of course, Einstein's interpretation had carried the day. There was no ether, so there was nothing to be entrained. The aberration of star light was simply a matter of observer-based geometry. Light from the star approached the observer at a given speed, the observer on earth moved in relation to the star at a certain velocity (depending on the star's direction in relation to the earth's position in its orbit at any given moment) and the light beam seems to approach at a small angle to its "true" direction, with a maximum angle of aberration of 20 seconds of arc.

This seemed to fit nicely with special relativity—so much so that Einstein was able to pull two tricks from one hat. Both the Doppler Effect and stellar aberration were derived using the same formula.[15]

It worked well—until binary stars were more closely studied. A special class of binary stars known as spectroscopic binaries had been discovered shortly before the special theory of relativity was published. Einstein may not have known about this discovery when he published his special theory.

There is unexpected drama here. For what we now know of binary stars has caused a problem for Einstein's theory. It may even be sufficient to undermine the special theory, or falsify it outright. The issue is explored in the next chapter.

Notes: Chapter 10

[1] Swenson, *Ethereal Aether*, 1972, p. 13.

[2] Banesh Hoffmann, *Relativity and its Roots*, p. 47.

[3] James Bradley, *Transactions of the Royal Society*, (1729), Swenson, op. cit., p. 14.

[4] Thomas Young, *Transactions*, (1804), Swenson, op. cit., p. 18.

[5] Dorothy Michelson Livingston, *The Master of Light*, pp. 83-84.

[6] Philipp Frank, *Einstein: His Life and Times*, Alfred A. Knopf, 1947, pp. 33-34.

[7] Gerald Holton, *Thematic Origins*, p. 285.

[8] French, *Special Relativity*, p. 44.

[9] Leo Sartori, *Understanding Relativity*, p. 41.

[10] Ronald W. Clark, *Einstein, The Life and Times*, World Publishing Co., 1971, p. 80.

[11] George C. Stokes, *Phil. Mag.*, (1846), Swenson, op. cit., pp. 23-24.

[12] A. A. Michelson, "The Relative Motion of the Earth and the Ether," *American Journal of Science*, v.3 no. 18, June 1897, p. 478.

[13] A. A. Michelson, "Relative Motion of Earth and Aether," *Phil. Mag.*, Dec. 1904, pp. 716-719.

[14] Petr Beckmann, *Einstein Plus Two*, p. 36.

[15] Einstein et al, *The Principle of Relativity*; "On the Electrodynamics of Moving Bodies," (1905), section 7, "Theory of Doppler's Principle and of Aberration," Dover 1952.

Chapter 11. Spectroscopic Binaries

Double stars are said to be as common as single stars. In 1804 the astronomer William Herschel showed that Castor, in the constellation Gemini, was actually two stars orbiting each other at close range. Herschel, like James Bradley a century earlier, had been looking for something else—stellar parallax again—but instead he found binary stars. In discovering for the first time that two stars circle each other around a common center of mass, he found the first evidence that gravitational influences exist outside the solar system.

Binary stars are important to astronomy because they are our best source of information on the mass and size of stars. The first double star to have been detected, much earlier than Castor, was Mizar, in the middle of the handle of the Big Dipper. Its double nature was seen in a telescope as early as 1650. But the Jesuit astronomer who discovered it did not have any reason to think that the two stars in his telescope were linked by gravitation. They could simply have been aligned along (almost) the same line of sight.

Much later, it was shown that one of the two Mizar stars, known as Mizar A, is also a double star, but of a special kind. Its component stars are so close together that they appear as a single star even in the most powerful modern telescope. Their dual character only becomes apparent when we examine their spectral lines. Spectroscopic binaries, as they are called, were first detected by the American astronomer Edward Pickering in 1889. In fact, Mizar A was the first spectroscopic binary to be detected.[1]

It is not clear that Einstein knew about spectroscopic binaries when he published his special relativity paper. The subject is important, because the evidence from binary systems may refute the special theory. It puts the theory in jeopardy at least. One cannot discount the possibility that the Einsteinians will find an escape but as things stand the evidence from binary stars seems to contradict the special theory.

Books on relativity rarely mention this controversy. But a recent work by Tony Rothman did discuss it, and papers on the subject have occasionally been published in professional journals.

The general public is not aware of the issue. Even specialists in the field are unlikely to be familiar with it.

The problem seems to have been first mentioned, and then only glancingly, by Herbert Ives in 1950. A contemporary of Einstein's, Ives was the director of optical research at Bell Labs, and one of the most eminent of the scientists to have disputed relativity theory. Once again stellar aberration is central. Ives touched on the issue in the following footnote:

"The idea sometimes met with that aberration . . . may be described in terms of the relative motions of the bodies concerned is immediately refuted by the existence of spectroscopic binaries with velocities comparable with that of the earth in its orbit. These exhibit aberrations no different from other stars."[2]

And that was all that he said.

Binary Mizar A

The binary system Mizar A is 88 light years distant from our Sun, and its luminosity is about 70 times that of the Sun. The two stars of Mizar A are so close that, even with the help of the largest telescope, they remain a single point of light and cannot be resolved visually into two stars. The stars are only 18 million miles apart—one fifth of the distance separating the Earth and the Sun.

We know they form a double-star system only because the rapid motion with which the stars orbit each other causes large alternating Doppler shifts in their spectral lines. They shift back and forth toward the blue and then the red ends of the visible spectrum. The cycle allows astronomers to determine the period of revolution of the stars. It is 104 days in the case of Mizar A. They orbit their common center of mass at a velocity of about 50 kilometers per second, or 1.7 times the Earth's orbital velocity.

Stellar aberration, as we have seen, refers to the small angular change in the direction of starlight caused by the Earth's orbital motion. James Bradley soon realized that the key variable explaining aberration is simply the Earth's orbital velocity. The angle of aberration is a function of the earth's velocity (30 kilometers per second) and the speed of light.

When the star's direction is perpendicular to the Earth's motion, its aberration is at a maximum and *all* stars in that direction have the same aberration. Six months later, when the Earth has turned 180 degrees in its orbit, and is heading in the opposite direction, the star's aberration had the same value but in the opposite direction.

In Newton's day and for many years later, the motion of the stars relative to the sun was not known. They were often referred to as the "fixed stars," in contrast to the planets. The constellations remained eternally unchanged. By the 19th century it was suspected that the stars themselves might be moving in relation to our solar system, but no one knew how fast or in what direction a given star moved. Anyway, the constancy of the angle of aberration for all stars (in a given direction), no matter how distant, strongly implied that any motion of the stars could be ignored in computing stellar aberration. The motion of the star with respect to our Sun was treated as an unknown "x" that existed on both sides of an equation and could be subtracted out without affecting the result.

When the wave theory of light was adopted, in conjunction with a universal ether, the speed of the light *source* was irrelevant anyway; for in classical ether theory the speed of a wave, whether of light, sound or water, is unaffected by the speed of the source that is creating the wave.

Einstein, however, had dismissed the ether as "superfluous" at the outset of his special theory. Further, he was obliged by his own postulates to regard the *relative velocity of the star and the observer* as the key variable causing the aberration. So that is what he did. He economically used the same method to derive *both* the formula for the Doppler Effect and the formula for stellar aberration.

But this meant that the stars' proper motion (if any) had to be factored in. In 1905, however, that was not a practical concern. Physicists still didn't have any information about the real motion of stars relative to the sun. In fact, in his own "Easy Einstein" book (written in 1916) Einstein discussed the matter in language that might have left laymen thinking that we have no reason to think the stars are moving at all. The special theory "enables us to predict the effects produced on the light reaching us from the fixed stars," he wrote. In the sentence that followed I have italicized the key clause:

> These results are obtained in an exceedingly simple manner, and the effects indicated, *which are due to the relative motion of the earth with respect to those fixed stars*, are found to be in accord with experience.[3]

If the stars really are "fixed," relative to the sun, then the only remaining motion of any consequence would indeed be the orbital motion of the Earth. And that does give results for aberration that is "in accord with experience."

But what if the stars are not really "fixed" at all?

Ritz Goes Ballistic

Mizar was discovered "only a few short years before Einstein's 1905 special relativity paper," Howard Hayden wrote. "Given the somewhat slow communications existing at the time, it is reasonable for Einstein not to have known about the existence of spectroscopic binaries."[4] Within a few years, however, Einstein did know about them. In 1913, the Dutch astronomer Willem de Sitter used information from binary systems to undermine the claims of Walter Ritz, who was advocating a ballistic theory of light as an alternative to Einstein's interpretation of Michelson-Morley. Einstein cited de Sitter's argument in his 1916 book.

What, then, is the relevance of spectroscopic binaries to Einstein's explanation of aberration? Even in cases where we still don't know what the true velocity of the binary system is, with respect to the sun, we do know that there is a difference, sometimes large, between the velocities of the two stars relative to us. In the case of Mizar A, we know that, at a given moment in its 104-day cycle, one star of the pair is moving toward us at the high velocity of 50 kilometers a second (relative to the center of mass of the binary system), while at the same moment the other star is moving away from us at the same velocity. Irrespective of the movement of the system as a whole, therefore, we know that the twin elements of the orbiting pair are moving at velocities that exceed that of the Earth's orbital velocity by quite a large margin. The side-to-side velocities are just as large, and they are the important consideration.

By Einstein's formula, large, alternating, back-and-forth aberrations should therefore be observed, corresponding to the period of their orbits. After a few weeks, the velocities of the rapidly orbiting stars will have reversed. Einstein's formula requires us to accept that the aberration angle of each star should increase and then decrease again as they circle each other. This would be easily observable by modern instruments. By Einstein's formula, the differential aberration would be so large that the stars would become visually separate and distinct in the sky before closing again.

In the case of Mizar A, Howard Hayden calculated that the angular separation of the binary components would be more than a minute of arc. But they always remain as an unresolvable point in the sky. And because binary systems are so common, we should be seeing this back and forth apparent motion of binary components all over the heavens. But we never do.

The issue of aberrated light from spectroscopic binaries is rarely discussed, but it has been the subject of at least two articles in the *American Journal of Physics*. The first was published in 1967, and the author was Edward Eisner. Like Herbert Ives, he worked for Bell Labs.

"It is widely believed that aberration, like the Doppler effect, depends on the relative velocity of source and observer," Eisner summarized. "If this were true, binary stars would mostly look widely separated and rapidly rotating. Not only is this not observed, but it would appear to conflict with Kepler's third law if it were," *i.e.*, it would violate the law of conservation of angular momentum.

In the main body of his article he wrote:

> [A]bout one star in three is a multiple system; so that the skies should be filled with binary stars of apparent separation of 40" [seconds of arc]. Indeed, such pairs should be seen circling distant galaxies many of which appear much smaller than that! And the apparent angular diameters of the orbits would increase with decreasing periods, which would be very spectacular and, incidentally, contrary to Kepler's third law.[5]

Thomas E. Phipps's article "Relativity and Aberration" was published by the same journal in 1989. Its purpose was "to expose and deal with the physical misconception that relative motion between radiation source (star, emitter) and sink (observer, detector) is responsible for observed stellar aberration."

The earliest explicit mention of the problem this created was that of Herbert Ives, Phipps wrote; Phipps's article would "reiterate Ives's point for the benefit of a new generation of physicists."

On a clear night, Phipps said, any optical astronomer "can refute by direct observation" the claim that the motion of the light source relative to the observer is the correct interpretation of the aberration formula. "If source motion mattered at all, observational astronomy would be a vestige of its present self and there would be no such thing as a *constant of aberration*."[6]

Tactfully, perhaps, Phipps avoided any mention of Einstein. He reserved his criticisms for "certain physics textbooks," some of them "pernicious," and leaving students "flatly misinformed."

Discussing the issue a few months before his death, Petr Beckmann said he doubted that this objection to special relativity could have been anticipated by Einstein; Beckmann had not even thought of it himself when he wrote *Einstein Plus Two*; nor had he ever seen it discussed. It was Howard Hayden who had brought it to his attention. Hayden's article, published in 1993, concluded by saying that "stellar aberration does not support special relativity theory, it contradicts special relativity theory."

In response to this challenge, published in *Galilean Electrodynamics*, a special correspondence section was devoted to the issue.[7] The defenders of Einstein mostly took the position that using the relative velocity of star and the Earth indeed gave the wrong result, but that Einstein had intended some other velocity to apply. But as we saw, Einstein in his popular account of relativity unambiguously said that his aberration formula applied to "the relative motion of the earth with reference to [the] fixed stars."

Aberration or Doppler?

But a second line of attack was available. To those who said that Einstein had intended another velocity, Hayden replied that Einstein's theory in that case gave the wrong result for the Doppler effect. For it had been derived almost in the same breath as aberration. In his paper, Einstein had given no indication that he was switching meanings for "v," (the velocity to which ambiguity attached, in the view of some critics). Therefore, switching the derivation of aberration from "guilty" to "innocent" meant that the Doppler derivation would have to be condemned instead.

One respondent, Milton Rothman, an emeritus professor of physics at Trenton State College, allowed that "the derivations of the aberration angle found in past textbooks do not solve the problem correctly." But, he said, "the fact that a single problem was handled inadequately does not invalidate Einstein's theory of relativity."[8]

In his book *Everything's Relative* (2003), Tony Rothman, the son of Milton, the author of several very readable books on science and a contributor to *Scientific American*, revived the issue. Einstein "clearly assumes that the velocity involved is the relative velocity between the Earth and the star," Tony Rothman allowed. The only problem is "it isn't true"; and therefore "the relative velocity of the star and the Earth cannot be the right one to use."

Boldly, Rothman concluded that "Einstein did not entirely understand his own theory." And since "no one bothers to read the original papers any more (all physicists *know* relativity)," he continued, "no one recognizes the rather large blunder in Einstein's exposition. This is not to say that the theory is wrong, just that Einstein didn't interpret it entirely correctly."

Einstein's "error," he added, "concerned nothing other than stellar aberration, one of the principal phenomena he devised the theory to explain."[9]

Howard Hayden replied that as far as he could see Einstein understood his own theory quite well, and applied it correctly. The problem was that it gave the wrong result. His theory, as applied to stellar aberration, "is in disagreement with fact."

By the time this issue of *Galilean Electrodynamics* was published, Petr Beckmann had only a few weeks left to live. During that time he was convinced that the aberration from binary stars unavoidably falsified special relativity.

"Einstein is dead," he said on his own deathbed. "But it will take decades to bury him."[10]

One final point: if the effect of the binary-star movements does not show up (when it should, in Einstein's theory), why should it *not* show up in Beckmann's theory? The answer is that his is an ether theory. The two light rays will at first travel with different velocities, "constant with respect to either star," Beckmann wrote. Thereupon they will

> stabilize at a common velocity as the gravitational fields of the two merge into one; the velocity will change to a different, but again common, value as the light enters the next dominant field on its journey, for it is still *c*, but now with respect to a different field; and so forth until it enters the telescope of a terrestrial observatory, with no reason for any special effects.[11]

Notes: Chapter 11

[1]   Background on double stars from George Abell, *Exploration of the Universe*, 4th ed., Saunders College Publishing, 1982, pp. 434-45.

[2]   Herbert E. Ives, "Extrapolation from the Michelson-Morley Experiment," *J. Optical Soc. Am*, April 1950, footnote, p. 190.

[3]   Einstein, *Relativity, The Special and the General Theory*, p. 49.

[4]   Howard Hayden, "Stellar Aberration," *Galilean Electrodynamics*, v. 4 Sept/Oct 1993, p. 92.

[5]   E. Eisner, "Aberration of Light from Binary Stars—A Paradox?" *American Journal of Physics*, 1967, p. 817.

[6]   Thomas E. Phipps, Jr., "Relativity and Aberration," *American Journal of Physics*, June 1989, pp. 549-50.

[7]   Correspondence, *Galilean Electrodynamics*, vol. 5, no. 2, Mar/Apr 1994, pp. 34-38.

[8]   Milton Rothman, *Galilean Electrodynamics*, vol, 5 and Hayden reply, p. 37, 38.

[9]   Tony Rothman, *Everything's Relative*, John Wiley & Sons, 2003, p. 74.

[10] Author's interview with Petr Beckmann, August, 1993.

[11] Beckmann, *Einstein Plus Two*, p. 37.

Chapter 12. On Beckmann's Theory

Perhaps the most surprising thing is that no one proposed the theory earlier. The underlying idea is so simple. The local gravitational field—whatever that is composed of—is also the ether or luminiferous medium—whatever *that* is composed of. Beckmann's great and simplifying idea was to propose that the one unknown is equivalent to the other.

The most important reason why this was avoided earlier, surely, was the "red flag" that prominently warned everyone to stay away from "entrained ether" theories. They were thought to have been ruled out by stellar aberration. If the ether were accompanying the Earth, no such aberration should have been detected.

But that objection applied to the 19th century ether of old. Beckmann had something different in mind: many local ethers, each one constituting the gravitational field of its own celestial body. With the old ether it would have been quite absurd anyway to suppose that the ether throughout the entire universe was being entrained by the orbital motion of mere planet Earth. Obviously there would have to have been a boundary, or border, beyond which the ether was *not* being entrained.

Michelson spent a good deal of time reflecting on the location of that boundary, which was why he tried experiments high up in the California Sierras. Maybe the entrainment would be reduced at a high altitude.

But if that boundary is at the zone where the gravitational field of the Earth blends into the field of the Sun, Michelson didn't go high enough! The intermediate zone must lie outside the orbit of the moon. And it is the relative motion between these adjacent fields that will transmit the angular change known as stellar aberration.

These fields merge into one another. Beckmann made the simplifying assumption of a sharp boundary, analogous to the skin of a bubble that encloses the Earth's gravitational field. As this "bubble" moves through the sun's field at the Earth's orbital velocity, he maintained, stellar aberration becomes visible to the astronomer on Earth.

Pokorny in Prague

Beckmann credits a physicist in Prague named Jiri Pokorny with having first proposed the key idea. In the 1950s he was one of Beckmann's graduate students. Later, he became professor of mathematics and physics at Charles University in Prague. Pokorny stayed in touch with Beckmann after he defected to the United States in 1963.

In the 1950s, Beckmann had expressed his dissatisfaction with the theory of relativity, mentioning in particular the null result of the Michelson-Morley experiment. How to explain it without abolishing the ether? "There are oodles of possibilities," Pokorny replied, in Beckmann's description years later. (They were speaking in Czech so he surely didn't use the word "oodles.") Pokorny added: "Maybe the gravitational field is the ether."

He just tossed it out as an idea. It was not something he had thought through. But Beckmann never forgot it. And when he retired from teaching at the University of Colorado, and had renewed attacks of what he called "Einstein-itis"—his recurring conviction that there must be a better path than the one taken by Einstein—he remembered what his old colleague had said.[1]

In 1954, Pokorny studied at the Faculty of Electrical Engineering at the Czech Technical University in Prague. Petr lectured on the propagation of electromagnetic waves. "His lectures were brilliant," Pokorny recalled, "his sense of humor was delightful." Later, Petr became head of a department in the Institute of Radio Engineering and Electronics, at the Czechoslovak Academy of Sciences.

> He created around him the right sort of scientific atmosphere. No conservative or dogmatic chains were put on our brains. He accepted the ideas of his collaborators, colleagues and employees and thought about them. Our brains were partners of his brain. He was always willing to change his mind, to acknowledge his own mistake. He provoked all of us to think about the unthinkable. His main criterion was truth. His spirit was impressed upon all people around him.[2]

In Boulder, Beckmann began to work in isolation on his theory, and it took him several years. The theory has been circulated quite widely among the "dissident community" of physicists. As we have seen, in addition to accounting for Michelson's null result, it generates a straightforward new prediction.

The gravitational field does not itself rotate every 24 hours along with the rotating Earth. So there is relative motion between the Earth and its field. But it is only a small fraction (one hundredth part, in mid latitudes) of the Earth's orbital velocity. This fraction must be squared, so the anticipated fringe shift is 0.00004 of a fringe, as opposed to the 0.4 of a fringe that Michelson expected. But this small fringe shift should be there.

When Beckmann published his book, he did not know that instruments were accurate enough to detect so small an effect. But an experiment with sufficient accuracy had by then already been conducted.[3] Amazingly, the principal researcher was a physicist at the University of Colorado in Boulder. His name was John Hall, and he even knew of Beckmann by repute. But Beckmann didn't know about the experiment, (described in chapter 23). John Hall received the Nobel Prize in Physics in 2005, but not for this experiment,

Great Minds Alike

Two other well known names were thinking along lines similar to Beckmann's. The first was Albert Michelson, who never accepted that the ether could be banished from physics. A later experiment by Michelson, carried out with the help of a colleague from the University of Chicago, Henry Gale, played a major role in leading Beckmann to his theory.

For twenty years Michelson contemplated the experiment that he ultimately carried out with the help of Gale.[4] When Beckmann was still in Prague, studying all the optical experiments bearing on relativity, he came across Michelson's brief report on his experiment with Gale in 1925. Beckmann referred to the experiment as a "symphony." Michelson theorized that the Earth's rotation would produce a fringe shift, just as Beckmann did years later. Michelson-Gale indeed did find this fringe shift. (See chapter 14.)

The other well known name was Albert Einstein. It is scarcely known today that Einstein revived the ether in 1916. He delivered a lecture on the subject at Leiden in 1920 and exchanged numerous letters with H. A. Lorentz. Einstein was not restoring the classical ether (as Lorentz wanted to do) but something new. It sounds remarkably like Beckmann's, with space no longer envisioned as a uniform void, but as something that varies according to location within the local gravitational field.

His 1920 lecture was reprinted in Einstein's *Essays in Science* in 1934,[5] but few laymen have heard of Einstein's new ether. Walter Isaacson's recent biography did acknowledge it, however.[6] The topic is reviewed at book length in Ludwik Kostro's *Einstein and the Ether* (2000), with a foreword by Max Jammer. After 1918, Einstein "expressed the identity of the gravitational field with the ether, among other things, by referring to the latter as *the gravitational ether*," Kostro wrote.[7]

Petr Beckmann never mentioned Einstein's restored ether and almost certainly didn't know about it. Yet it seems more than possible that Beckmann's ether, construed as the local gravitational field, was anticipated by Einstein himself. The subject is reviewed in chapter 21.

There is nonetheless an important difference between them. As Einstein had already shown, light really does not travel in straight lines at a constant speed. It travels in gravitational fields of varying density, where it changes direction. Light rays "propagated across a gravitational field undergo a deflexion," as Einstein wrote in 1911.[8]

But by then Einstein had already published his special theory, in which light is treated as though it inhabits a gravity-free world. To avoid repudiating special relativity, therefore, Einstein had to embed this crucial finding of his general theory within complex general tensors and differential geometry. Much of this complexity could have been avoided, Howard Hayden has said, if Einstein had not felt obliged to uphold his earlier commitment to the fictitious ideal of a constant speed of light.

Beckmann's theory is not so encumbered. He accepts from the outset that light bends and slows in denser gravitational fields. He could therefore describe everything more simply, and we poor mortals are no longer obliged to conjure up something that is as impossible to imagine as curved four-dimensional space-time. As Edward Teller asked, at the event commemorating Petr Beckmann:

> What does it mean if three dimensional space, and even more horribly, four dimensional time-space, is curved? That you won't understand very readily.[9]

The 19th century ether implied that absolute motion through space could be detected. But with Einstein's relativity, it became axiomatic that that cannot be true. Beckmann, despite his general dissent, does not restore absolute motion. If the single uniform ether of old is replaced with lots of local ethers, distributed throughout space, all we can say is that a body is in motion with respect to a particular field. But we cannot identify motion in an absolute sense. There is no ultimate reference frame to which motion can be referred. To this extent then, Einstein's theory remains undisturbed by Beckmann's. On the other hand, the idea of a single time, flowing uniformly for all observers, irrespective of their relative states of motion, is restored. In Einstein's theory, all observers moving in relation to one another are allocated their own times.

Special, General and Real

Another important point is that the distinction between special and general relativity that is so central to Einstein ceases to have much meaning in Beckmann's theory. The inertial reference frame always was a convenient fiction anyway. We may be better off without it. In all earthbound experiments, the force of gravity is present, and the idea that it can be ignored for the sake of argument is a conceptual weakness of special relativity (as Einstein himself recognized). Objects moving or even stationary on the surface of a rotating Earth are unavoidably subjected to gravitational and centrifugal forces.

For this reason, as Howard Hayden has pointed out, the Einsteinians can claim exemptions from the rules of special relativity whenever they are faced with experimental results that disagree with the theory. This was the fate of the Sagnac experiment, as we shall see, and that of Michelson and Gale, and others. In these cases, Beckmann liked to say, the Einsteinians found they could disassociate themselves from unfriendly data by retreating into general relativity "like guerrillas disappearing into the jungle."

The identification of the ether with the gravitational field is itself sufficient to blur the distinction between the two kinds of reference frames—inertial and non-inertial. Beckmann's theory implies that light travels neither at a constant speed nor in a straight line; for it *always* travels in a gravitational field. In contrast, the key postulate of special relativity is that light travels at a constant speed (as long as it never feels the influence of a gravitational field).

For Beckmann, light slows down and bends as it enters a denser field. It straightens up as it moves into the rarefied field of outer space, where the field becomes attenuated. The new theory restores the analogy between light and sound, the speed of which is also affected by the density of the medium (air) in which it travels.

Einstein's general theory also accepts that light rays bend in proximity to a gravitating body; that was its most famous prediction. The difference is that Einstein needed complicated math and "curved space-time" to reach that result. Beckmann arrives at the same conclusion by classical physics.

Beckmann's *Einstein Plus Two* scarcely registered on the academic radar screen. "I am afraid they are not going to attack me," Petr told me before his death. But the book sold well, and its major argument was understood, by a number of well qualified physicists, including Edward Teller. He acknowledged its "pleasing features" in a public talk he gave memorializing Beckmann, in August, 1993.

Notes Chapter 12

[1] Quotations from Beckmann, not otherwise attributed, from the author's interviews with him between 1988 and 1993.

[2] Jiri Pokorny letter to author, February 7, 1995.

[3] A. Brillet and J. L. Hall, "Improved Laser Test of the Isotropy of Space," *Physical Review Letters*, v. 42, 26 February 1979, pp. 549-552

[4] Michelson and Gale, "The Effect of the Earth's Rotation on the Velocity of Light, part II," *Astrophys. Journal*, April 1925, pp. 140-45.

[5] Albert Einstein, *Essays in Science*, Philosophical Library, 1934, p. 98.

[6] Walter Isaacson, *Einstein: His Life and Universe*, Simon & Schuster, 2007, p. 111.

[7] Ludwik Kostro, *Einstein and the Ether*, Apeiron, Montreal, 2000. p. 184.

[8] Einstein et al, *The Principle of Relativity*, Dover, p. 107.

[9] Edward Teller's talk was reprinted in *Access to Energy*, vol. 21, October, 1993.

Chapter 13. The Sagnac Experiment

Georges Sagnac, professor of theoretical physics at the University of Paris, assisted Pierre Curie in determining the properties of radium, and before that was familiar with Michelson's experiments. By 1904, Michelson had published an article suggesting new experiments that should show the elusive fringe-shift. It is not known whether Sagnac saw this paper, but he carried out such an experiment and it did show a fringe shift. His results were published in two articles in the journal of the French Academy of Sciences, *Comptes Rendus*, in 1913. The first was titled "The luminiferous ether demonstrated by the effect of the relative motion of the ether in an interferometer in uniform rotation."[1]

Books about relativity have shown little interest in Sagnac's experiment. Nonetheless, it is easily understood, and what is now known as the Sagnac Effect is undisputed. It has been demonstrated since Sagnac's time (1869-1926) with great accuracy and has found an application in ring-lasers. Since the 1980s fiber-optic gyroscopes in commercial aircraft have used the Sagnac Effect as a navigational device.[2] Sagnac corrections are also built into the Global Positioning System.

His apparatus consisted of a horizontal platform about 20 inches in diameter, with a light source and an interferometer with four mirrors at the perimeter. The apparatus could be rotated, like a large record turntable. Two light beams were sent around the platform at the same time, from one mirror to the next, in opposite directions. They were reunited, as in earlier interferometer experiments, and the combined light beams showed the familiar pattern of interference fringes. Then, as the platform rotates, the position of the fringes begins to shift. As the speed of rotation increases, the fringe shift also increases.

Howard Hayden and Cynthia Whitney explained the fringe shift as follows:

> From the standpoint of the laboratory frame, light traveling in the same direction as the mirrors spends extra time catching up to the mirrors, while light traveling in the opposite direction spends less time because the mirrors catch up to [i.e. approach] the light. A

phase shift results. From the standpoint of the moving mirrors, we note that the distance from one mirror to the one ahead or behind does not change; therefore the measured fringe shift must be attributed to a non-isotropic velocity in that reference frame.[3]

Isotropic means the same in every direction.

In relativity theory, this should not happen. The speed of light is supposed to be the same in all reference frames, irrespective of the movement of the source or the observer. It is always and everywhere said to be isotropic, according to Einstein. So the simple explanation of the Sagnac effect, by which is meant the fringe shift—that the speed of light is *not* a constant—must be rejected by the Einsteinians. Indeed, an article in *Physics Today* describing the Sagnac effect calls the above explanation "simple-minded."[4] (Meaning it has no recourse to relativity theory.) Nonetheless, it "gives the Sagnac phase shift correctly," the author adds. Wisely, he spared *Physics Today* readers the tortuous explanation involving general relativity.

In Sagnac's simple interpretation, then, the light ray moving opposite to the direction in which the apparatus was rotated is moving (in relation to the approaching mirror) slightly faster; in the other direction, the light ray is moving (in relation to the receding mirror) slightly slower.

The following analogy may help us to see how this implies the existence of an ether. Instead of Sagnac's apparatus, imagine that we have a merry-go-round at a circus. There is an entrance point, from which two people walk around in opposite directions at identical speeds. Each touches a wooden horse before moving on to the next. Both follow an identical path, and we are required only to assume that they find a way to avoid bumping into one another half way around. Not only will they return to the starting point at the same time, but this outcome will be unaffected by the rotation of the merry-go-round. That is because the floor-boards to which everything is attached go around along with everything else.

Now imagine a merry-go-round with a difference. It is suspended a few inches above a lake, and the pair who start together at the entrance can no longer walk along floor boards to reach the next wooden horse, because there are no floorboards. Instead they must swim through water. They swim at identical speeds, relative to the water, and once again the merry-go-round rotates. The wooden horses and the starting point all go around together, but the water remains stationary. This time, the array of wooden horses will be moving toward one swimmer, and away from the other. So the swimmers will *not* meet again at the starting point. The shift in the point at which they do meet corresponds to the Sagnac Effect.

The water, of course, is equivalent to the ether. Sagnac assumed that he had demonstrated its existence. The shift in the position of the interference fringes, he wrote, "ought to be regarded as a direct manifestation of the luminiferous ether."

At the end of his first article for *Comptes Rendus* he wrote: "The observed interference effect is clearly the optical whirling effect due to the movement of the system in relation to the ether and directly manifests the existence of the ether, supporting necessarily the light waves of Huygens and Fresnel."[5]

In his analysis of the early reaction to special relativity in Europe and America, Stanley Goldberg wrote that "there was virtually no response to the theory of relativity *per se* in France during the years between 1905 and 1911."[6] Henri Poincaré had not mentioned it, and Goldberg speculates that "it is difficult to believe that the silence in France was not influenced by Poincaré's attitude."[7] In his 1913 papers, Sagnac likewise gives no sign of having encountered Einstein's special theory. The general theory would not be published until 1916.

Einstein knew about the Sagnac experiment, however. In a short article, published in 1914, he discussed it, and in his discussion, according to a modern commentator, he "recognizes the need for distinguishing between two distinct vacuum speeds of light in certain non-inertial systems." That surprising comment, by E. J. Post, was published in *Physics Today* in 1982. He had written a major article about the Sagnac effect for *Reviews of Modern Physics* in 1967.[8]

Indeed, at the end of section 2 of his paper on general relativity (1916) Einstein had written: "The principle of the constancy of the velocity of light *in vacuo* must be modified."[9] Max Abraham, a strong supporter of relativity, "took Einstein to task (in a rather unfriendly manner) about this deviation from his earlier stance," Dr. Post adds. "Abraham's objections have now been forgotten, because they were an attempt at curtailing a researcher's privilege to change or even modify his earlier views of nature."[10] But Abraham had a point. For a scientist who lays down the law, and then later quietly informs us that that law is only true in special cases (inertial reference frames, in this instance) has weakened his own case.

E. J. Post wonders how we are to explain the discrepancy "between what Einstein said and what most of us today understand him to have said," especially given "all this evidence militating against the universal constancy of the speed of light in vacuum." Accepting a universally constant speed of light is justifiable "*at best* as a theoretical extrapolation," Post writes. Oddly, he concludes with the comment that the real cause of the problem is the lack of an "easily accessible complete collection of Einstein's original papers."

Twenty five years after Post's comments were published, this complete collection still does not exist. (Only ten out of a projected 25—or possibly 30—volumes of the Collected Papers had been published, over 50 years after Einstein's death.) Dr. Post's reference to Einstein's 1914 paper is certainly valuable. Few would have known about it otherwise.

Anyway, Einstein made his comment on the Sagnac Effect an occasion to amend his famous claim about the constancy of the speed of light. And when we look at the classically derived explanation of the Sagnac effect, and see that it falls afoul of special relativity because it involves a speed of light that is greater than c, we have reason to think that the classical explanation of the Sagnac effect may be the best explanation.

Wolfgang Pauli, a strong Einstein advocate, mentioned the Sagnac experiment in his 1921 book on relativity, and was one of the few who did so in the early years. His comment is misleading, I believe. He writes:

"Particularly worth mentioning is Sagnac's experiment, in which all parts of the apparatus are rotated together, because it shows that that the rotation of a reference system relative to a Galilean system can be determined [detected] by means of optical experiments within the system itself."

He concludes—and here is the misleading part: "The result of this experiment is in perfect agreement with the theory of relativity."[11]

The canonical view of the Sagnac experiment today is that, because the apparatus is rotated, we have a non-inertial reference frame. Therefore the special theory does not apply. We must use instead the general theory. It's as though the general theory comes to the rescue of the special theory.

In classical Newtonian physics—which has its simplest expression in inertial systems—scientists routinely do calculations within non-inertial systems such as in rockets and on the rotating earth. The Coriolis Force, for example, gives rise to cyclonic storms which turn counter-clockwise in the Northern Hemisphere and clockwise in the Southern. In all cases, the *amount* of acceleration enters the calculations.

But special relativity has no provision whatsoever for doing calculations within non-inertial systems. No matter how large or small the acceleration, there is no way of incorporating it into the equations. It is treated only as a *true/false* variable. If there is no acceleration (which is *false*), then the equations of special relativity are supposed to apply. If there is any acceleration whatsoever (which is *true*), then one must use the general theory. We will see several examples of this logical quandary in this and succeeding chapters.

Petr Beckmann analyzed the experiment in a late paper published five years after *Einstein Plus Two* came out.[12] He concluded that general relativity could indeed explain the Sagnac effect, but also that the explanation based on classical physics was far simpler. Einstein's explanation is correct, Beckmann concluded, "in the sense that it predicts accurate numerical values." But the price was high:

"Apart from the loss of conceptual transparency, the introduction of a complicated tensor calculus, and the unnecessary use of Riemannian geodesics (Fermat's principle works in Euclidean space with no complaints), [general relativity] has to work with the 'proper' time rather than with the simple and transparent 'local' time."

In short, a mountain had given birth to a mouse. "So let us now discard the mountain and let the mouse be born by a mouse," Beckmann went on. We "discard the equivalence principle, Reimannian space, tensor potentials and the rest of the erudite General Relativity apparatus." Sagnac's own explanation sufficed. "His ether need only be replaced by the gravitational field."[13]

Beckmann also pointed out that the classical explanation is capable of wide generalization. It explains the effect simply by asking "by how much the frame has rotated during the round trip" of the light rays. The question "is so simple and so penetrating that the round trip need not be made by light."

The eighteen survivors of Ferdinand Magellan's three-year round-the-world trip found on their return that they had "lost a day" when they compared their own journals (arrived at by starting a new day with a new sunrise) with the calendar in Seville, Beckmann wrote. In traveling west they had been "rotating" against the direction of the earth's rotation, and therefore each day seemed slightly longer than a day in Spain. But general relativity cannot allow a comparable explanation because the spherical Earth is non-Euclidean and so it must "attribute the lost day to curved space and proper time. There is no way it can present an equally simple method covering both Magellan's and Sagnac's experience."[14]

Beckmann acknowledged that Einstein's roundabout method gave "accurate numerical values," and was willing to dispute the claims of other anti-Einsteinians on this point, some of whom believe that the Sagnac effect cannot be explained by relativistic means. But Beckmann saw that it was sufficient to claim that his own reinterpretation of the ether as the local gravitational field, together with the common-sense explanation of the Sagnac Effect, gave not only the same answer as general relativity, but gave it far more simply. This put him in the stronger position of accepting rather than contradicting all the other evidence that is used to confirm general relativity. He merely pointed out that it could all be interpreted more simply.

Beckmann noted that Einstein's mathematical apparatus was "quite redundant since the same result can be derived in a few lines of elementary mathematics on the simple hypothesis that the velocity of light is constant with respect to the gravitational field through which it propagates."

This way of looking at the matter has been confirmed in a modern textbook on optics, by Eugene Hecht, who teaches physics at Adelphi University. In the third edition of his *Optics* he boldly derives the Sagnac Effect "using classical reasoning." On the page, he then works through the "few lines of elementary mathematics" that Beckmann had mentioned. Hecht prudently adds:

> The preceding classical treatment is obviously lacking, inasmuch as it assumes speeds in excess of c, an assumption that is contrary to the dictates of Special Relativity. Furthermore, it would appear that since the [Sagnac] system is accelerating, General Relativity would prevail. In fact, these formalisms yield the same results.[15]

They reach the same destination, either by a simple or a complex route. Take your pick. But it is gratifying that Hecht chose the straightforward path in his textbook.

The Michelson-Morley experiment was more ambitious than Sagnac's, because Michelson attempted not just to detect the existence of the ether but to quantify the interferometer's passage through it. In contrast, Sagnac's table-top apparatus was too small to have been able to do that. He merely detected its existence. He did consider a more elaborate experiment, but he soon realized that he would need very much larger or more sensitive apparatus. He never performed that experiment.

Michelson did. By 1904 he had concluded that his famous experiment with Morley had been based on an unproductive assumption: that the Earth's orbital velocity was the measure of the relative motion of the Earth and the ether. But if the ether was accompanying the orbiting Earth, that was obviously wrong. Nonetheless, Michelson considered it unlikely that this ether was *rotating* with the Earth's rotation. Therefore, relative motion between Earth and the ether might be measurable after all.

Michelson knew of a way to do the experiment. It was based on an idea similar to Sagnac's, with two light rays going in opposite directions around an enclosed area and meeting up. But unlike Sagnac, Michelson would not have to rotate his apparatus. The Earth itself would provide the rotation. In 1924, Michelson teamed up with another member of the physics department at the University of Chicago to put this theory to the test. This was the Michelson-Gale experiment, carried out in the winter of 1924-25 in Clearing, Illinois. It is even less well known than the Sagnac experiment.

Notes Chapter 13

1   Georges Sagnac, *Comptes Rendus*, (Paris, 1913), pp. 708-10, 1410-1413. Reprinted in *The Einstein Myth and the Ives Papers*, Devin Adair Co., Greenwich, 1979, pp. 247-250.

2   "Sensitive fiber-optic gyroscopes," *Physics Today*, October 1981, pp. 20-22.

3   Howard Hayden and Cynthia Whitney, "If Sagnac and Michelson-Gale, Why Not Michelson-Morley?" *Galilean Electrodynamics*, vol. 1, Nov/Dec 1990, p. 1.

4   *Physics Today*, op. cit., p. 20.

5   Sagnac, *Comptes Rendus*, op. cit.

6   Goldberg, *Understanding Relativity*, p. 216.

7   Goldberg, op. cit., p. 217.

8   E. J. Post, "What Happened to Einstein's Papers?" *Physics Today*, June 1982, p. 11; and "Sagnac Effect," *Reviews of Modern Physics*, April 1967, pp. 475-493.

9   Einstein et al., *Principle of Relativity*, Dover, p. 114.

10 Post, *Physics Today*, June 1982, p. 11.

11 W. Pauli, *Theory of Relativity*, (1921), Pergamon Press, 1958; Dover, 1981, p. 19.

12 P. Beckmann, "Sagnac and Gravitation," *Galilean Electrodynamics*, v. 3 Jan/Feb 1992, pp. 9-12.

13 P. Beckmann, "Sagnac and Gravitation," op. cit.

14 P. Beckmann, "Ockham, Magellan and Sagnac," *Gal. Electr* vol. 2, 1991, p. 82.

15 Eugene Hecht, *Optics*, 3rd edition, Addison-Wesley Longman, Inc. 1998, p. 428.

Chapter 14. The Michelson-Gale Experiment

The Michelson-Gale experiment was the most remarkable of all Michelson's experiments, and the least remarked. Rarely is it mentioned, even in physics textbooks. By then chairman of the Physics Department at the University of Chicago, Michelson was assisted by Henry Gordon Gale. He was said to be part of Chicago's "wintry trio of astronomers," Hale, Gale and Frost.[1] Within a few years, Gale succeeded Michelson as head of the department.

His new theory predicted a displacement in the interference fringes once again, even though such a prediction had failed in Michelson-Morley. But the new experimental design was quite different, and this time a fringe-shift was detected. Theory and experiment were in agreement. Or so Michelson initially thought.

By 1904, he had formed an opinion about the ether that was quite different from the one he had held 20 years earlier. His original theory had been that Earth goes through the ether with a velocity at least equal to its orbital velocity. Later, he concluded that the ether was carried along with the Earth,[2] but it might not rotate with the Earth's rotation. If it did not, there should be a detectable motion of the ether relative to the Earth. The rotational velocity of the Earth in the latitude of Chicago is about 700 miles per hour.

The new experiment, therefore, was designed to measure an effect produced by a velocity that is about one hundredth of its orbital velocity. To detect it, the apparatus had to be much larger than anything seen earlier. In fact, it enclosed a rectangle 2010 feet from east to west, and 1113 feet from north to south.

An attempt was made to do this experiment at the Mt. Wilson Observatory, in 1923, but air currents caused the interference fringes to be unstable. Michelson realized he would have to use evacuated tubes—a considerable expense. To help meet it, the city of Chicago provided pipe a foot in diameter and over a mile long. Light rays, deflected by mirrors at the corners, traveled through the tubes throughout the entire length of the apparatus.

Michelson's daughter wrote that after months of preparation the experiment "took place at Clearing, Illinois, on the prairie some ten miles west of the university, in the bitterly cold weather of early December, 1924." For much of the time Michelson was not well, and he depended on Henry Gale.[3] He took on the toughest assignments, and his "dogged devotion was one of the reasons Michelson insisted that the results be published under their joint authorship."[4]

The Most Grandiose Experiment

Sixty years later, Beckmann observed that Michelson's new theory was substantially the same as his own: that the local gravitational field is equivalent to the ether. The Earth's field "translates" with the Earth, but it does not rotate with its rotation; therefore a fringe-shift is to be expected. Michelson was essentially testing this theory. Beckmann was enthusiastic about the experiment. It was

> surely the most grandiose interference experiment ever performed: its optical path length amounted to something like 10^{14} wavelengths, traversed with what was then considered 'monochromatic' light: the light from a carbon arc passed through a filter. Michelson's feat, which to my knowledge has never been repeated, is both a technical masterpiece, and one that provides fundamental insights into the optics and electromagnetics of moving sources. Yet it rarely makes it into the textbooks, certainly not into the introductory ones.[5]

It had features in common with Sagnac's experiment. Two beams of light were sent in opposite directions around the huge rectangular path. Looked at from the point of view of the apparatus (pipes and so on) the distance around the rectangle is the same clockwise as it is counterclockwise. But from the point of view of the ether (gravitational field) that permeates everything, including the pipes, the two light paths are not the same. Light will take slightly longer to go one way than the other. A fringe shift should result.

Why this difference in velocity? It is caused by the different latitudes of the two east-west legs—even though they are only about a fifth of a mile apart. As the Earth rotates, the east-west leg closer to the equator moves faster (relative to the ether, or gravitational field) than the leg further to the north.

The ether "wind" on the surface of the Earth goes from east to west, because the Earth rotates to the east. So the counter-clockwise light beam moves into a stiff ether wind as it goes east, but feels a weaker ether wind on its back as it goes west along the northerly track. The clockwise light beam is less handicapped. The eastbound beam along the northerly path meets a weak ether wind, and then going back west has the stronger wind behind it. So the two circuits are unequally affected, and that is the source of the fringe shift.

Consider two runners racing in opposite directions around a mile-long rectangle. A soft wind blows to the west across the northern part of the track, and a stronger wind blows in the same direction along the southern part. Running that race, it would make a difference whether you chose to run clockwise or counterclockwise. Contestants equal in other respects would not return to the starting point at the same time if they ran in opposite directions.

The experiment detected a displacement of about a quarter of a fringe in the interference pattern, a value within three percent of what the theory had predicted.

The fringes had shifted, but in relation to what benchmark? Einstein himself admired Michelson's ingenuity in solving this problem. Since the Earth continuously rotates, it was obviously not possible to move the Earth back and measure how much the fringes had shifted away from their original position. Michelson solved the problem by adding a smaller rectangular path for another set of counter-rotating light beams. One of its arms was shared with the larger rectangle. "The area enclosed by this circuit was much too small to give a measurable displacement," Michelson wrote, and it could therefore act as "a fiducial mark from which to measure the displacement [in the larger circuit]."[6]

Einstein knew about the experiment and favored its completion. Visiting Chicago in 1921 he discussed its value with Michelson.[7] In a 1953 letter to Robert S. Shankland, a professor of physics at Case Western Reserve, Einstein said that his "admiration for Michelson's experiment is for the ingenious method to compare the location of the interference fringe pattern with the location of the image of the light source. In this way he overcomes the difficulty that we are not able to change the direction of the Earth's rotation."[8]

It is said that Michelson was in the end unenthusiastic about his own experiment. It is important to understand why. Harvey B. Lemon, a friend of Michelson's, describes the meeting at the University of Chicago in which Michelson gave his assent to go ahead with the project. "Well gentlemen," he remarked, "we will undertake this, although my conviction is strong that we shall prove only that the Earth rotates on its axis, a conclusion which I think we may be said to be sure of already."[9]

Michelson Not Enthusiastic

Shankland gave an explanation for this coolness, but not the correct one. "Michelson's poor health and the excessive newspaper publicity that attended this experiment cooled his enthusiasm for the work, but it was carried through successfully," Shankland wrote.[10]

The truth was that 20 years earlier, in 1904, Michelson had believed that an experiment with contra-rotating light beams would indeed show the displacement of the fringes and would therefore demonstrate, finally and unequivocally, that there really was "this medium known as *the ether*," as a technical assistant to Michelson wrote. Sagnac, too, had taken his result as demonstrating that the ether is real. The Sagnac result seemed incompatible with special relativity. A visible fringe shift was *not* an outcome that had been anticipated by Einstein. According to special relativity, not only does the ether not exist, but the speed of light is supposed to be ever the same in a vacuum, irrespective of its direction or of the movement of the observer, or of the experimental apparatus.

After Sagnac's result was known, however, and even before Michelson-Gale, the Einsteinians perceived two things. First, there were grounds for claiming that the special theory did not apply. The conditions were non-inertial, because the apparatus was rotating, on the table-top in the case of Sagnac; and the Earth was rotating around its axis in the case of Michelson-Gale. The equations of special relativity could not incorporate an acceleration even as small as the three-thousandths of one-*g* experienced in the experiment.

Second, the *general* theory of relativity could be brought to the rescue. It could explain both the Sagnac effect and a fringe shift caused by the Earth's rotation. It did so by new methods, with complicated mathematics, and with conceptions of space and time that few could grasp. By such means, then, the relativists were able to turn the tables on the etherists. They could argue that the experiment *would* show a fringe-shift and this would constitute one more triumph for relativity—general relativity. Far from falsifying special relativity, it would confirm general relativity!

There is evidence that Michelson had for some time wanted to do an experiment that would falsify relativity. He considered relativity a "monster" and had anticipated a result that would be difficult for Einstein and supporters to explain. Henry Gale wrote that the Michelson-Gale experiment was one "which Professor Michelson had wished to try for years."[11]

But as time went on and the experiment approached, we read that Michelson agreed to do the experiment "out of deference to the desires of some advocates of the theory of relativity."[12] Among them, was Einstein himself. The University of Chicago also "brought pressure" on Michelson. His daughter was 14 years old at the time of the Einsteins' visit, and she recalled some details in her book.[13]

According to a memo from Henry Gale to the university's vice president, "this experiment has roused international interest to a very unusual degree as it is expected to furnish another check on the truth of the Einstein Relativity Theory. Professor Michelson's reputation will ensure a very large amount of highly desirable publicity to the University if this experiment is carried out."[14]

What Chicagoans had in mind was more of the publicity of a few years earlier. Eddington's eclipse observations had confirmed the prediction of general relativity that starlight would "bend" as it passed by the sun. The University of Chicago was looking forward to a comparable flood of attention. For Michelson, however, special relativity and its apparent abolition of the ether had upset his whole worldview. That his new experiment would give one more shot in the arm to the "general" version of Einstein's "monster" was about the last thing he had intended.

The leading promoter of the idea that Michelson-Gale would constitute one more confirmation of general relativity was Ludwik Silberstein, a mathematical physicist with the Eastman Kodak research laboratory in Toronto. In 1921 he wrote an article for the *Journal of the Optical Society of America*, on "The Propagation of Light in Rotating Systems." Its mathematical arguments, Michelson "modestly professed he was unable to dispute," Harvey Lemon wrote in his obituary appreciation of Michelson.[15] That didn't help either, because the word soon spread that Michelson, although an acknowledged maestro with lenses, mirrors and monochromatic light, was out of his depth when it came to theoretical physics.

Silberstein had persuaded Michelson to go to Toronto to discuss the project, and even offered to pay for the whole experiment. In the end, he contributed only $500 (or $491.55, as Michelson pointedly noted in his otherwise sparse paper in *The Astrophysical Journal*).

Dorothy Michelson Livingston paints an unflattering portrait of Silberstein, no doubt reflecting her father's sentiments. It particularly bothered all those out in the field (and it literally was a field) that Silberstein showed up at the experimental site in Clearing with "an unwelcome covey of reporters."[16] Michelson always distrusted them, and in this instance he had reason to do so.

The Einsteinians had turned the tables on Michelson, and this was the source of his growing discontent. What was originally thought of as an experiment that would use the Earth's rotation to demonstrate the ether—non-existent according to special relativity—and would therefore potentially disconfirm the theory, had been turned into one more likely confirmation of the general theory. If it showed a fringe shift, the general theory would triumph anew; and if it showed no fringe shift then Einstein's special theory would be re-confirmed. Moreover, Michelson's theory of an ether entrained by the Earth's orbital motion but not by its rotation would be falsified.

Not surprisingly, the reporters who had come to the site were not sure which way to report the experiment. When the fringe shift was confirmed, the *New York Times* had these confusing headlines:[17]

MICHELSON PROVES EINSTEIN THEORY
Experiments Conducted with 5200-Foot
Vacuum Tube Show Light Displacement

ETHER DRIFT IS CONFIRMED
Rays Found to Travel at Different Speeds
When Sent in Opposite Directions.

Michelson at one point described the experiment as a crucial test for general relativity. In the *University Record* he reported that if the fringe-displacement "should turn out to be zero . . . it would be exceedingly difficult if not impossible, to account for the Einstein theory."[18] But in his paper for the *Astrophysical Journal*, Michelson refused to interpret the result and shunned all theoretical analysis.

In the end, all sides agreed that the results were equally consistent with ether theory or with general relativity. Einstein noted this himself in his letter to Shankland,[19] and Harvey Lemon agreed: "Both classical theory and the theory of relativity predicted the same results."[20] Michelson took the same line: "This result may be explained on the hypothesis of an ether fixed in space, but may also be interpreted as one more confirmation of Einstein's theory of relativity."[21] Perhaps that was why the experiment received so little attention later.

An article in the *American Journal of Physics* in 1994 discussed the Sagnac effect and other experiments using contra-rotating light beams, and added some little known details.[22] The authors point out that such experiments had been discussed by the eminent British physicists Oliver Lodge and Joseph Larmor in the late 19th century.

"In articles published in 1893 and 1897, Sir Oliver Lodge clearly anticipated the Sagnac result in general as well as the associated possible detection of Earth rotation in an interferometer of area 1 square kilometer." To be sure, the authors added, Lodge and Larmor were discussing these ideas "within the now obsolete confines of an ether-theoretic model." Henry Gale also noted that the Michelson-Gale experiment "had been suggested by Sir Oliver Lodge."[23]

What this suggests, however, is that the solution to the great quandary of theoretical physics caused by the Michelson-Morley null result had been grasped by eminent physicists such as Lodge and Larmor even before the theory of relativity was proposed.

As to the Michelson-Gale experiment, what reason is there for regarding the "ether-theoretic model" as obsolete? Einstein himself had revived it, only a few years earlier. Its supposed "confines" appear more liberating than restricting today. That is especially so if we regard the criterion of simplicity as arbitrating between theories that are equally competitive in other respects.

Petr Beckmann pointed out this difference between the ether-based explanation of Michelson-Gale, and Einstein's. The classical explanation "follows from the Galilean principle of [relativity] in a few lines of high school algebra, whereas Einstein's general theory does it with multidimensional complex tensors in space-time and non-Euclidean geodesics."[24]

Notes: Chapter 14

[1]   Dorothy Michelson Livingston, *Master of Light*, 1973, p. 186.
[2]   Albert A. Michelson, *Phil. Mag.*, 1904 pp. 716-19.
[3]   Livingston, op. cit. p. 308.
[4]   Livingston, op. cit., p.310.
[5]   Petr Beckmann, *Einstein Plus Two*, p. 44.
[6]   Michelson and Gale, *Astrophysical Journal*, April 1925, pp. 140-45.
[7]   Livingston, op. cit., p. 290.
[8]   Robert S. Shankland, "Michelson and His Interferometer," *Physics Today*, April 1974, p. 41.
[9]   Harvey B. Lemon, "Albert Abraham Michelson: the man and the science," (1936); see Dover edition of Michelson's *Studies in Optics*.
[10] Shankland, op. cit., p. 41.
[11] H. G. Gale, "Albert A. Michelson," *Astrophys. J.* 1931, pp. 1- 9 (1931).
[12] Lemon, op. cit., foreword, p. xiii.
[13] Livingston, p. 290.
[14] Livingston, p. 290.
[15] L. Silberstein, "Propagation of Light in Rotating Systems," *J. Optical Society of America*, pp 291-307, (1921); Michelson, quote in H. B. Lemon, foreword to *Studies in Optics*, xiii.
[16] Livingston, p. 310.
[17] *New York Times*, Jan 9, 1925. Swenson, *The Ethereal Aether*, p. 208.
[18] Livingston, p. 309.
[19] *Physics Today*, April 1974, p. 41.
[20] H. B. Lemon, op. cit., xiii.
[21] Loyd Swenson, *Ethereal Aether*, p. 207.
[22] R. Anderson, H.R. Bilger, G. E. Stedman, "Sagnac effect: A century of Earth-rotated interferometers," *Am J. Phys*, **62**, Nov. 1994, pp. 975-985.
[23] *Am J. Phys.* op. cit., (1994) fn. 24.
[24] Beckmann, *Einstein Plus Two*, p. 45.

Chapter 15. Mesons, Muons and Time Dilation

The critic of any theory is obliged to counter it at its strongest, and some think that atomic particles called mesons are special relativity's prize exhibit. Often you see them referred to as muons, a later name, with a more refined understanding of the particle. Here, they will be used interchangeably. The electron was discovered in 1897, and about fifty years later the meson made its bow. It was "the first of the electron's heavier brothers," Abraham Pais wrote. "The muon is still one of the strangest animals in the particle zoo, yet its discovery was liberating, too, since it made possible an understanding of certain anomalies in the absorption of cosmic rays."[1]

A Japanese physicist, Hidekei Yukawa, wrote an article in the 1930s suggesting that a new atomic particle was needed to account for the atom's cohesion. New particles (such as quarks more recently) usually seem to start out this way—as theory-saving devices. Then, when physicists know what to look for, they often find them. (The outer planets of the Solar System were initially deduced to explain anomalies in the orbits of visible planets.)

The posited particle was thought of as something alternately grappled by protons and neutrons. George Gamow, an outstanding writer who overlapped with Petr Beckmann at Boulder in the 1960s (Gamow died in 1968), realized that only with metaphors could we visualize particle physics. He came up with a good one for mesons:

> The best one can do is to imagine two hungry dogs who come into possession of a juicy bone and are grabbing it from each other to take a bite. This tasty bone is continuously passing from the jaws of one of them into the jaws of the other, and in the resulting struggle the two dogs become inseparably locked.[2]

The idea was that the attractive forces within the atom "are due to a similar struggle for possession of that tasty particle." It could be electrically neutral, or carry a positive or a negative charge. Nobody believed it at first, but then Carl Anderson at Caltech discovered particles of the appropriate mass in the cosmic rays "showering down to the ground from the upper reaches of the atmosphere."

The newcomer was first called a heavy electron, then a light proton; finally it was named *meson*, against the protest of a French physicist who did not want it to be confused with *maison*. The particle picture soon became more crowded with the introduction of pions, neutrinos and quarks, but we shall ignore them.

After mesons were discovered, experiments in 1940 showed that lots of them were to be found arriving high up in the Rocky Mountains. But not so many reached Denver, 5000 lower in elevation. Enrico Fermi suggested that the undercount was due to the mesons' instability. Mesons are radioactive, and break down into other things (electrons and neutrinos) within a split second. A comparison between the numbers of mesons that were detected at two elevations, one at Echo Lake, 10,000 feet up, and the other at Denver, allowed their "half life" to be calculated.[3]

Mesons studied on the ground showed they have a half-life of about 2.2 millionths of a second. But with their earthly duration so short, they should have decayed while still in the atmosphere. None would survive long enough to reach the ground. But plenty of them made it to Denver. So now there was an opposite problem. How to account for their profusion?

It was decided that their normal decay rate is like a clock. At the end of every "tick," if the half-life is 2.2 microseconds, half the mesons have disintegrated into electrons and anti-neutrinos. So the conclusion was that when traveling at a high speed, mesons live longer. "Time" in their reference frame is slowed down. An experiment in 1963 used arrays of counters at the two different elevations. Their results were said to be in good agreement with special relativity, which predicts that time slows down in the moving reference frame, as observed from the frame of the Earth. In *Understanding Relativity*, Leo Sartori refers to muons instead of mesons, but he is talking about the same thing.

> The muon lifetime experiments provide strong evidence for the reality of time dilation. No other plausible explanation has been suggested for why so many of the muons should survive a trip that lasts much longer than their rest half-life; that is, for why the half-life of muons in motion is longer than for muons at rest. Special relativity accounts for the results in a straightforward manner.[4]

Actually, another plausible explanation was suggested—inadvertently. George Gamow himself was responsible. As he was a friend of Einstein's and an orthodox relativist, we can be sure that he intended no heresy. But he said quite plainly what surely does happen with the fast-moving mesons. His error (I mean from the relativists' point of view) only shows how thin is the barrier separating the counter-intuitive world of relativity physics from a more straightforward way of looking at the world. Gamow said:

> Slowing down of all physical processes in fast-moving systems was observed directly in the case of the decay of mesons, the unstable elementary particles which constitute an essential fraction of cosmic rays coming down to the surface of the earth at extremely high speed.[5]

It surely is the *physical processes* that slow down, not "time." The process of decay within the atomic particle as it flies through the Earth's gravitational field is slowed down by its transit through that medium. In the same way (as we shall see) the light wave from the distant star that passes close by the sun is slowed down and thereby "bent," or refracted by the Sun's gravitational field.

If the relativistic outlook is correct, then we must abide by relativity's principles, the first of which—the principle of relativity—imposes the same result observed from the other reference frame. If we were to fly toward the Earth with the speeding meson, we would (by Einstein's theory) observe everything proceeding more slowly on the Earth's surface. We would also observe the spatial contraction of the Rocky Mountains before we were brought to an abrupt halt by the granite surface. No such observations have been made from the "other" reference frame, however, and until they are, the relativists are in a weak position when they claim that the speeding mesons have confirmed their theory of time dilation.

Imagine an observer who travels with high speed toward the Earth in such a fashion. Imagine also that he observes time dilation and length contraction on the Earth. The Rocky Mountains are reduced to one tenth of their vertical height, for example. Would we say that such changes on the Earth are "real" or only "measured"? It is an awkward question for the relativists.

In his detailed study of the special theory, Arthur I. Miller claims that the "various experiments involving elementary particles [such as mesons] involve a vicious circle because their data analysis depends on special relativity; consequently these experiments test only the consistency of the special theory of relativity."[6] Petr Beckmann says more or less the same thing.[7] But it seems that the objection applied only to the early meson experiments in the 1940s.

Ives-Stilwell Experiment

Miller proceeds to make the remarkable claim that "to this day the Ives-Stilwell experiment is the only positive proof for Einstein's prediction of time dilation."[8] Miller's book was published in 1981, and the Ives-Stilwell experiment was in 1938. Moreover, Ives himself never accepted relativity and put a different interpretation on his experiment with Stilwell.

Herbert Ives (1882-1952), director of electro-optical research at the Bell Labs, became more and more critical of relativity as the years passed. It is difficult to explain the Ives-Stilwell experiment, which observed the Doppler shifted frequencies of hydrogen ions from a single source but traveling in opposite directions. It was "an object lesson in what can be done by skilled investigators pushing a technique to its limits," wrote A. P. French in his book on special relativity. "It is a curious sidelight on this experiment that its authors did not (even as late as 1938) accept special relativity theory," French added. "In their view the result simply demonstrated that a moving clock runs slow (as Larmor and Lorentz had suggested) . . . Old and cherished ideas die hard."[9]

Petr Beckmann analyzed the experiment in his own book, and came to the conclusion that what it demonstrated was that particles traversing a gravitational field radiate (in their own rest frame) a frequency reduced by a factor dependent on their own velocity through the field. Its effect is to give the time difference that would also be found by transporting a cesium clock through the gravitational field.[10]

Beckmann pointed out that supposed measures of time dilation always fail to ask if the effect depends on the observer's location, "or is it something that changes the clock?" To illustrate the point, he imagines two identical *pendulum* clocks whose time readings are compared after one of them has been transported around the globe. If flown eastward, the transported clock will read fast. If flown westward, it will be slow.

Time dilation? Not so, says Beckmann. "The period of a pendulum varies inversely as the square root of the downward force on it, and that force is the vector sum of gravitational attraction and the centrifugal force due to the earth's rotation." That force must (slightly) increase when the clock moves eastward, because its angular velocity about the earth's center increases; and it must decrease when transported westward. "This is an *inherent* change, one that an observer traveling with the clock (i.e. at rest with respect to it) could measure by comparison with an equally accurate wrist watch – if it is unaffected by centrifugal force."[11] He cites this as a change in a clock "which might easily be mistaken for a change in the flow of time."

The same argument will apply to the atomic clocks flown around the earth in opposite directions; and later on board the satellites of the Global Positioning System. Here indeed, to repeat Gamow's words, "slowing down of all physical processes was observed directly," as the clocks moved through the Earth's gravitational field.

Contraction not Observed

Meanwhile length contraction, one of the most famous predictions of relativity, has not yet been observed, either in the heavens or upon Earth. Pictures of foreshortened space-ships flying at high speed are all imagined by artists. Hendrik A. Lorentz, who had proposed such contraction, said in 1910 that relativistic length contraction was something that could "actually be observed" in photographs.[12] But Arthur I. Miller said that "almost half a century later James Terrell (1959) showed that the contraction of a moving body in the direction of its motion could not be seen on a photograph."[13]

More recently, David Park, physics professor of Williams College, threw in the towel on length contraction. "Nature is less generous with flying yardsticks than with flying watches," he wrote.[14] But that has not prevented some writers from believing that length contraction has been observed.

In *The Roots of Relativity*, for example, Banesh Hoffmann considers what would be seen by an observer who "keeps pace with the muons." Since they are stationary relative to him, he will not observe any slowing of their decay rates. "But he—and the muons—will see the mountain rushing toward them with almost the speed of light, and therefore relative to them the mountain will be contracted so that the distance between its top and its bottom will be much shorter than for the observer on the ground."[15]

Hoffmann considered that these observations were real. "The muon experiment is a versatile one," he went on. "It confirms three relativistic predictions: the slowing of clocks, the contraction of lengths, and the similar relativistic behavior of all types of clocks."

But no observations have yet been made from the point of view of the moving muon. Beckmann predicts that such a test would show clocks on Earth running fast relative to muon clocks. For if the physical processes of the muon are really slowed down by their motion through the field, Earth clocks would obviously show no such retardation. They just sit there on the Earth's surface, not minding how swiftly muons come rushing at them. Nor will their readings be affected if these fast approaching particles are accompanied by observers with cameras and recording equipment.

So the two theories make quite different—opposite—predictions. In relativity, the observed clock change is attributed to its motion with respect to an observer; Beckmann's theory describes real effects as physical things move through the field.

Beckmann liked to say that almost all physics experiments have been carried out on Earth-bound laboratories, which in turn are "nailed to the gravitational field." Therefore, as a first approximation, the two theories would predict the same outcome—most of the time. For if one observes something moving in a laboratory (where the observer is located), one also observes it moving with respect to the gravitational field. But when we turn to an experiment in space—looking at Earth clocks from the perspective of speeding muons, for example—relativity theory and "gravitational field" theory predict opposite outcomes.

Notes: Chapter 15

[1]   Abraham Pais, *'Subtle is the Lord'* ..., p. 359.

[2]   George Gamow, *The Biography of Physics*, Harper & Bros, 1961;
      p. 314; reprinted as *The Great Physicists From Galileo to Einstein*,
      Dover.

[3]   Gamow, *The Great Physicists*, pp. 316-18.

[4]   Leo Sartori, *Understanding Relativity*, p. 82.

[5]   Gamow, *The Great Physicists*, pp. 178-79.

[6]   Arthur I. Miller, *Albert Einstein's Special Theory*, p. 251.

[7]   Beckmann, *Einstein Plus Two*, p. 98.

[8]   Miller, op. cit., p. 251.

[9]   A. P. French, *Special Relativity*, p. 146.

[10] Beckmann, op. cit., pp. 78-81.

[11] Beckmann, op. cit., p. 78.

[12] Miller, op. cit., p. 213.

[13] James, Terrell, "Invisibility of the Lorentz Contraction," *Phys. Rev.*
      116, 1041-45, (1959), Miller p. 251.

[14] David Park, *The How and the Why,* Princeton, 1988, p. 284.

[15] Banesh Hoffmann, *The Roots of Relativity*, p. 110.

Chapter 16. Hafele and Keating

Special relativity predicts that time will run more slowly for a flying clock than for an identical stationary clock. The "twin paradox," in which one twin travels at high speed and returns younger than the other, expresses the idea of time dilation more colorfully. No such experiment with twins has been done, but by the 1970s atomic clocks were accurate enough to investigate the question: When an atomic clock is moved, does it run more slowly than a stationary clock?

This was put to the test in October, 1971, by J.C. Hafele of the Washington University in St. Louis; and Richard Keating of the U.S. Naval Observatory in Washington. Atomic clocks were transported in opposite directions around the globe on commercial flights. The first leg of the eastbound journey, for example, was a Pan Am flight from Dulles Airport to London. Atomic clocks, on loan from the Naval Observatory, were simply placed on passenger seats of a Boeing 747.

"The experiment may be the cheapest ever conducted to test the general theory of relativity; it cost some $8000, of which $7600 was spent on air fare," the *Scientific American* reported.[1]

The ability to do the experiment at all depended on the accuracy of cesium-beam clocks. They measure the passage of time "by extremely regular pulses of electricity emitted by oscillating crystals," the *New York Times* reported. These oscillators "are in turn kept at an even more regular rate by the radioactive decay of cesium atoms."[2] The clocks kept time to within 26 billionths of a second (nanoseconds) per day, but more recent atomic clocks are capable of even greater accuracy.

When the clocks returned home, the time shown by the traveling clocks was compared with the one that remained in Washington. No comparisons were made during the flight.[3]

The usual claim is that the Hafele-Keating experiment confirmed Einstein's prediction. The results "were in excellent agreement with the predictions based on relativity," Leo Sartori wrote.[4] The experiment gave "remarkable results," Ralph Baierlein noted—and indeed it did. He, too, found "excellent agreement between theory and experiment."[5]

J.C. Hafele himself said something rather different. The true prediction of relativity theory "seems to have been largely overlooked in the past," he wrote.[6] How so? A "quite remarkable feature" of the theory is that of "directional dependence" for time dilation. The "relativistic time offset accumulated by a clock during circumnavigation of the Earth depends both on the direction of the circumnavigation and on the Earth's rotational speed." This indeed was new. Except that Beckmann's theory said exactly that.

Steven Hawking's comment, mentioned earlier, in which he joked that if one wants to live longer one should keep flying to the east, referred to the Hafele-Keating experiment.[7]

Expect the Unexpected

The U.S. Navy provided the clocks; Hafele was mainly responsible for the theoretical work. It is clear from his articles, including one that he sent to *Nature* 18 months *before* the clocks were put on the planes, that he already knew what would happen. He warned readers ahead of time to expect the unexpected. "The standard answer that moving clocks run slow by the well known factor [given by the Lorentz transformation] is almost certainly incorrect," he foresaw.[8]

What were the actual results? The west-bound clock sped up, gaining 273 nanoseconds. The east-bound clock slowed down, losing 59 nanoseconds—both compared to the clock that stayed in Washington. Einstein had said nothing about time-dilation depending on the direction in which a clock is moved. "Moving clocks run slow"—that was the Einstein mantra. But atomic clocks reveal that when they are moved, some go slow and some go fast. It all depends on whether they go east or west.

The authors might have been tempted to say that Einstein's theory seemed to be wrong. Or they could have claimed that the conditions ruled the experiment out as a valid test of special relativity (a point I shall return to). In fact what they did was to visualize another reference frame, compared with which it truly *could* be said that the "moving clocks ran slow." By this means they rescued Einstein's theory, at least outwardly.

Here is how they did it. We must watch closely, because Einstein's theory, as formulated in 1905, is about to be adjusted in a way that brings it closely into line with Beckmann's.

The experiment was described in two articles in *Science,* on consecutive pages. The first paper set forth the "predicted relativistic time gains"—in which an "interesting asymmetry" was foreseen.[9] The second paper reported the "observed relativistic time gains." The publishing arrangement was unusual. The purpose seems to have been to prepare (and reassure) readers that nothing unanticipated was about to be presented. Without this heads-up, readers might indeed have been surprised. For the results did not conform to relativity theory as it had been understood until that time.

The authors first noted that special relativity predicts that "a moving standard clock will record less time" than clocks "at rest in an inertial reference space." But because the Earth rotates, clocks stationary on the Earth's surface "are not suitable" to be considered as inertial. Therefore, the flying clocks must be compared *not* to the Naval Observatory clock in Washington but to the "hypothetical coordinate clocks of an underlying nonrotating (inertial) space."[10]

Underlying nonrotating inertial space. That is a mouthful, but an important one. Clifford Will, in his account of the experiment, said (like Hafele) that the comparison clock in Washington was non-inertial, so "we can't simply compare the flying clock directly with the ground clock." Instead, we must "compare the rates of both clocks to a set of fictitious clocks that are at rest with respect to the center of the Earth."[11]

Einstein's theory has now and henceforth been quietly changed—adapted to the real world, one might say. No longer is it motion with respect to the *observer* that causes time dilation. It is motion with respect to a real block of space within which the Earth is embedded and rotates. Operationally, as readers may have guessed, the *underlying non-rotating inertial space, at rest with respect to the center of the Earth* is the same thing as the *local gravitational field* of Beckmann's theory.

In interpreting this experiment, J.C. Hafele, Clifford Will and others gave a posthumous Einsteinian imprimatur to the idea that a set of synchronized clocks is spread across this local field of underlying inertial space. Visualize it as a block of space enclosing the Earth, but not rotating with the Earth. In order to detect our old friend time dilation what we must do is compare the time told by the airborne clocks with the time told by this set of fictitious clocks.

If we assume that the faster the airborne clocks move in relation to those "fictitious" ones, the more the moving clocks will slow down, then the "remarkable results" of Hafele-Keating will seem to correspond with Einstein's theory. For the "moving clocks" will indeed slow down, as they are expected to do. And that is how the experiment has been interpreted ever since.

Einstein's Theory Amended

Nonetheless, Einstein's theory has been amended in a crucial way. The old idea was that the effect-producing motion (yielding time dilation) was with respect to the *observer*. That has now been changed to motion with respect to the underlying nonrotating inertial space.

This may be visualized as follows. Imagine that we are looking down on a classroom globe from a point above the North Pole. The globe is placed on a circular carpet and rotated to the east (counter-clockwise, seen from above). The eastbound plane has taken off from Washington and is crossing the Atlantic. It is heading in the same direction that the globe is rotating, so we must *add* its speed to that of the rotating Earth. We can now see that the plane is moving quite rapidly in relation to the carpet beneath it.

The carpet is equivalent to the nonrotating inertial space, or the gravitational field.

Now visualize a westbound plane, going from Washington to Los Angeles. Its direction is opposite to the Earth's rotation. As we look down from above, it might not be moving at all relative to the carpet. It all depends on its airspeed. If it were the Concorde, yes, it would "really" be flying to the West. It would be seen to move not just across the surface of the globe, but also against the background of the carpet. But if it were flying slower than the Earth is rotating, it would look (from above) as though it were flying backwards relative to the carpet. Flying at about 700 mph, it would appear to be stationary against the background of the carpet.

Meanwhile, the Washington observatory, stationary on the Earth, is also moving around with the Earth's rotation. So it, too, is moving against the carpet background. So we have three speeds relative to the carpet. The eastbound plane is moving quickly against that background; the Naval Observatory clock is moving at an intermediate speed; the westbound plane is moving only slowly against the carpet's background.

So the more rapidly the clock was moving in relation to the carpet, or the Earth-centered non-rotating space, the slower the clock ran compared with the "fictitious" clocks of the non-rotating space.

It's the Clocks, Not Time

Petr Beckmann's theory says the same thing. In his case, however, it is a dynamic interaction between the flying clock and the local gravitational field that causes *the clock* (not time) to slow down. What changes the oscillation rate within the atomic clock is its movement through the gravitational field. The oscillations slow down with motion through the field, and they slow down to a greater extent when that speed increases. We would therefore expect the eastbound clocks to slow down much more than the westbound ones. The Washington clock itself also moves through the field, at about 700 miles per hour in the Washington latitude. So that clock "slows down," too. The westbound clock will lose the least amount of time. And that is what the experiment showed.

A. P. French, whose book on special relativity preceded Hafele-Keating by a few years, said there was something "misleading" about the familiar claim that "moving clocks run slow." The phrase suggests "that some essential change occurs in the operation of the clock itself, that the physical basis of its operation has somehow been modified." It is a central feature of relativity theory that "just the opposite is true—that the operation of the clock as described in its own frame of reference is completely unaffected."[12]

But in Beckmann's theory there really has been "some essential change" in the operation of the clock. The relative motion of the gravitational field through the guts of the atomic clock slightly impedes its rate of oscillation. A dynamic cause is postulated.

Analyzing this and related experiments, Howard Hayden asked, "Yes, moving clocks run slowly, but is time dilated?"[13] He noted the analogy with a pendulum clock being transported around the globe. Eastbound, it would be subjected to a higher centrifugal force, and so it would slow down. This illustrated "the real slowdown of clocks for which the cause is a real phenomenon, as opposed to an artifact of one's particular coordinate system." Yet In the Hafele-Keating experiment, investigators "do not ask, let alone answer, whether *time itself* is dilated or processes are simply slowed by moving through the gravitational (or in some cases, magnetic) field."

It's worth noting that atomic clocks transformed relativity theory. Theorists were forced by the actual functioning of moving clocks to abandon the old idea that time dilates in reference frames that move in relation to the observer. Instead they had to refer time differences to clocks in a block of non-rotating space. They had recourse to something they had long abjured—a preferred reference frame. All reference frames were not created equal after all. As we shall see, GPS also depends on utilizing the Earth-centered inertial reference frame.

There is an additional complication, and it, too, will apply to GPS. The higher elevation of flying clocks causes them to speed up relative to ground-level clocks. When we take into account the effects of altitude on clock rates, general relativity enters the picture. This is why it not easy to say whether the Hafele-Keating experiment tested special or general relativity. In the usual interpretation, both were involved.

After take-off, when the plane reaches a higher altitude, the gravitational field thins out. In its attenuated state, the field acts as less of an impediment to the action of the atomic clocks. Therefore they speed up relative to clocks on the ground or flying at a lower altitude. It's analogous to the reduced air resistance at greater altitude, which is why jets consume less fuel when they fly high.

Dr. Hafele told the *New York Times* before the first flight that, although the clocks in flight were expected to run more slowly, the "latest calculations show that the gravitational effect might offset this. The [general] relativity prediction holds that time would pass more slowly in a strong gravitational field than in a weak one. The stay at home clock in Washington will be subjected to a stronger gravity than the four airborne clocks because of the altitude difference."[14]

The offsets of motion and altitude were of comparable magnitude. It was predicted that the eastbound clocks would *lose* 184 nanoseconds as a result of motion through the field, but *gain* 144 nanoseconds because the field is thinner at a higher elevation. So the pre-flight prediction was that the eastbound flying clocks would lose 40 nanoseconds altogether. The measured figure turned out to be 59 nanoseconds, which was considered to have been close enough.

Westbound, the slow motion of the clock relative to the gravitational field was already causing the on-board clocks to gain time relative to the one in Washington. And the thinner gravitational field at cruising altitude caused the flying clocks to gain even more time. So these two corrections had to be added together. This prediction, too, was confirmed experimentally, showing a net gain of 273 nanoseconds westbound.

Results Known Beforehand

Some final comments on this fascinating experiment: One interesting features is that Hafele and Keating figured out what was going on before the experiment was formally conducted. Hafele's paper in *Nature*, submitted in February, 1970, and published that July (the clocks were not flown until October, 1971), showed that he knew ahead of time that the clock retardations had to be referred to a non-rotating Earth-centered frame. This gave him the east-west asymmetry that matched the facts. Hafele also gave the physics community a timely warning: anomalous results were to be expected. He gave another warning in a second article, published by the *American Journal of Physics* in January 1972, a few months before *Science* published the data. In his *AJP* article, submitted before the atomic clocks were even into put the planes, he noted (correctly, I believe) that the predicted result "seems to have been largely overlooked in the past." Overlooked by Einstein, that is.

It is said that the authors of science papers often know the results before they carry out their experiments, and this was surely true of Hafele and Keating. A footnote to their first *Science* paper suggests this.[15] They mention "previous trips with cesium beam clocks" that lasted "several days to weeks" and these gave "closure times with a spread of about 60 nanoseconds per day or trip." This itself is footnoted to a technical publication, *Proceedings of the Second Annual Precise Time and Time Interval Strategic Planning Meeting*, published in 1970 and available from the U.S. Naval Observatory in Washington. I have not seen it, nor have I seen this point discussed in the literature.

It is everywhere claimed that the rotation (with the Earth) of the Naval Observatory clock rendered its frame non-inertial, thereby disqualifying it as a test of special relativity. So the earth-centered inertial space was substituted. But the clocks on the planes could also have been disqualified by the same reasoning. They too were circumnavigating the globe.   There wasn't an inertial frame anywhere in sight, Howard Hayden said. By strict Einsteinian rules the whole experiment could have been ruled out of court. It was nonetheless admitted into the canon of relativity-confirming experiments, perhaps because a reinterpretation of its "remarkable results," seemed compatible with relativity. But the reinterpretation was decidedly more compatible with Beckmann's theory.

If we take the Hafele-Keating result as correct, then the monetary reward offered by Beckmann and Hayden to anyone who can show that the speed of light is the same to the east as it is to the west, can hardly be collected. For the east-west time differential that Hafele-Keating found is simply the atomic-clock analogue of an east-west light-speed differential.

Notes Chapter 16

[1] "Time Flies," *Scientific American*, September 1972, pp. 67-68.

[2] Harold M. Schmeck Jr., "Airborne Atomic Clocks to Test Einstein Time Theory," *New York Times*, October 2, 1971. "They Beat the Clock Checking on Einstein," *New York Times*, October 8, 1971.

[3] "A Question of Time," *Time*, October 18, 1971.

[4] Leo Sartori, *Understanding Relativity*, p. 200.

[5] Ralph Baierlein, *Newton to Einstein*, p. 278, 281.

[6] J.C. Hafele, "Relativistic Time for Terrestrial Circumnavigations," *American Journal of Physics*, January 1972, p. 81, 84.

[7] Stephen Hawking, *The Universe in a Nutshell*, Bantam Press, 2001, p. 9.

[8] J.C. Hafele, "Relativistic Behavior of Moving Terrestrial Clocks," *Nature*, July 18, 1970, p. 271.

[9] J. C. Hafele and Richard E. Keating, "Around-the-World Atomic Clocks: Predicted Relativistic Time Gains," *Science*, 14 July 1972, pp. 166-67. "Around the World Atomic Clocks: Observed Relativistic Time Gains," *Science*, op. cit. pp. 168-70.

[10] Hafele and Keating, op. cit., p. 166.

[11] Clifford Will, *Was Einstein Right?* p. 54.

[12] French, *Special Relativity*, p. 105.

[13] Howard Hayden, "Yes, moving clocks run slowly, but is time dilated?" *Galilean Electrodynamics*, July/August 1991, pp. 63-66.

[14] *New York Times*, Oct 2, 1971.

[15] Hafele and Keating, op. cit., pp. 167-68, footnote 7.

Chapter 17. Global Positioning System

Almost overnight, the Global Positioning System became the trump card of relativity. Relativistic corrections are built into the system, we are told, and the system works. With such practical uses as surveying and navigation, GPS not only brings theoretical physics down to earth, it tells us where on earth we are. GPS puts relativity "deep in the machine," said Harvard's Peter Galison. "In a trading zone of engineering-philosophy-physics, relativity had become a technology, one that swiftly displaced traditional surveying tools."[1]

"There is no better illustration of the unpredictable payback of fundamental science than the story of Albert Einstein and the Global Positioning System," Clifford Will said. "[T]he next time your plane approaches an airport in bad weather and you just happen to be wondering, 'what good is basic science,' think about Einstein and the GPS tracker in the cockpit, guiding you to a safe landing."[2]

For anyone skeptical of relativity, surely, GPS is a critical test.

The Global Positioning System is a navigation and timing system of 24 satellites in Earth orbit, each carrying atomic clocks. Orbiting 11,000 miles above the Earth's surface, they complete two circuits every 24 hours. They move in six orbital planes, each at an inclination of 55 degrees to the equator; in each plane there are four equally spaced satellites. They move at 3.87 kilometers per second, in a reference frame that is unaffected by the Earth's rotation. The orbiting satellites can be thought of as a tracing out a skeletal cage, within which the Earth rotates on its axis.

Satellites must be about ten degrees above the horizon if their signals are to be received clearly. The arrangement ensures that at any given time, eight satellites are within the line of sight of an observer anywhere on Earth. When signals from four satellites reach the receiver, the user's position can be calculated to within a few feet.

How does it work? If the satellites' positions are known relative to the Earth, and if we also know the instant at which the signals are sent, the receiver's position on Earth can easily be calculated. The signals are radio waves, which travel at the speed of light.

GPS satellites, first launched in 1977, are operated by the Department of Defense. The Pentagon has the capability of "dithering" the signal, so that for some years reception for civilian use was limited in accuracy to 100 meters. By 2000, however, the value of GPS to the public was such that President Clinton turned off the "selective availability" and made the highest precision available to all.

Accurate navigation by GPS would not be possible without modern atomic clocks. If navigation errors of more than a meter are to be avoided, according to Neil Ashby of the University of Colorado, "an atomic clock must deviate by less than 4 nanoseconds from perfect synchronization with the other satellite clocks. That amounts to a fractional time-stability of better than a part in 10^{13}. Only atomic clocks can do that. Even so, the system requires frequent uploads of clock corrections to the satellites."[3] Light travels one foot in a nanosecond.

Prof. Ashby has in recent years been the leading academic expert on the relationship between relativity and the GPS, and his *Physics Today* article, published in 2002, is often cited. I shall quote from it, and from one or two other articles he has written in recent years.

Much simplified, the system works by applying the formula: Distance (from satellite to the observer) is equal to speed (of light) multiplied by time (taken for the signal to reach the observer). Suppose the signal from one satellite is in transit for a tenth of a second. The receiver's locus can then be anywhere on the arc of large circle—the signal has traveled 18,600 miles in all directions in that fraction of a second. A simultaneous signal from a second satellite will locate the receiver on a second arc. The signal from a third should pinpoint the user's position. A fourth signal allows the receiver to correct its clock, which is not nearly as precise as the atomic clocks in the sky.

The signals are sent from the satellites in a steady stream, and the system has an ingenious way of distinguishing one signal from another. The times at which the transmissions originate "must be established by a self consistent synchronization scheme," Neil Ashby wrote.[4] Synchronization of the orbiting clocks is therefore crucial.

But here's the problem. Einstein said that clocks moving relative to one another *cannot* be synchronized. Leo Sartori put it exactly that way in his *Understanding Relativity*: "Clocks in relative motion cannot be synchronized." Why not? Such clocks "keep time at different rates," Sartori said. Even if they could be synchronized at one instant, "they would not stay synchronized."[5]

This is the famous problem of the "relativity of simultaneity," found in the Easy Einstein books. It is a direct consequence of Einstein's assumption that the speed of light is a constant, whatever the observer's motion. This in turn obliges us to accept that time proceeds at different rates for the observers of differently moving clocks.

Examining the problem "of synchronizing a rest clock with a moving clock," Jeremy Bernstein warned, "'time' in the moving frame will differ from 'time' in the rest frame." He put the word "time" in quotation marks to let us know that there is no such thing as one simple time. "There is nothing to be done about this," he added."[6]

Nonetheless, GPS clocks that are moving in different planes with respect to the equator *are* moving with respect to each other. Furthermore, with each passing moment, all these clocks are moving at varying speeds with respect to an observer on the Earth's surface. If we accept a strict interpretation of Einstein's doctrine, it would seem that there is indeed "nothing to be done." Clock synchronization would be impossible and the system wouldn't work.

Relativistic Corrections?

In fact, when the GPS was in the planning stage some consultants raised this objection and there was real uncertainty as to whether the system would work. Ashby himself served as a GPS consultant in the 1970s, and he reports that making corrections to the system to bring it into line with relativity theory was "controversial." Some "believed you had to account for it; some didn't," he writes. So divided were the designers of the system that the first GPS satellite was launched without the frequency offset, but they had "a switch to turn on the offset just in case."[7]

Corrections were duly entered, and the moving atomic clocks indeed remained synchronized. The key question here is whether it was appropriate to call these corrections "relativistic."

There is an inherent problem in establishing that even stationary remote clocks are synchronized. They are synchronized if they tell the same time at the same instant, but if the speed of light is itself the top speed at which we can send messages, how can we know that distant clocks are telling the same time at any given moment?

As Leo Sartori wrote. "If simultaneity is defined in terms of clock readings, how can the simultaneity of the clock readings themselves be verified? The argument appears to be circular."[8] One way might be to synchronize adjacent clocks, then move them apart slowly. But that is unsatisfactory because, "we cannot be sure that motion does not affect synchronization." In fact, Einstein's theory maintains that it does, no matter how slowly they are moved.

The conventional Einsteinian method is to solve the problem by fiat. A signal is sent from point A (at time 1) to point B. Then it is reflected back to point A (returning at time 2). Clocks A and B are said to be synchronized by deciding that the signal arrives at point B at time 1.5, half way between times 1 and 2. Or you can assume that clocks are "Einstein synchronized" if light signals from two remote points reach the midpoint between them at the same instant.

But both assume that the speed of light is the same in all directions. And that is the very point at issue. In special relativity the speed of light *is* the same in all directions—but by postulate. Einstein assumed it was so. Physical observation came later, and it has shown otherwise.

The issue was put to the test, experimentally, when orbiting satellites and atomic clocks made it possible to send radio waves around the world. The signal went east from a point (in Colorado) to a GPS satellite, thence to another point over the horizon (in West Germany), on to another satellite; then to a location in Japan; and from there back to Colorado. This was repeated in the opposite direction. Ashby and co-authors published the results in *Science* in 1985. They found that the signals took unequal times to go around the world in opposite directions.

This result remains the same "whether slowly moving portable clocks or electromagnetic signals are used to complete the circuit," Ashby, Allan and Weiss wrote. "A portable clock transported slowly eastward once around the earth's equator will lag a master clock at rest on the earth's surface by 207.4 nanoseconds; if transported westward the portable clock will lead by about 207.4 nanoseconds."[9] This was essentially the same result that Hafele and Keating had obtained in 1971. But electromagnetic signals and satellites made the exercise much more reliable and accurate.

The Ashby experiment was conducted by the National Bureau of Standards in Boulder, Colorado. Ashby was (and remains) a professor at the University of Colorado. Petr Beckmann, then in Boulder himself, was working on his book on relativity and was not always keeping up with the latest findings. He had no idea (until later) that an experiment, undertaken at Boulder, had confirmed that light travels at different speeds east and west.

Not surprisingly, then, synchronization of GPS clocks could not be achieved using the strict assumption of a light speed that is constant in all directions. If you try to "Einstein synchronize" a series of clocks around the globe, the last will turn out to be out of synch with the first.

Suppose you send a radio wave around the globe at the equator, west to east, in an attempt to synchronize clocks along the path. "Traversing the equator once eastward, the last clock in the synchronization path would lag the first clock by 207.4 nanoseconds," Ashby wrote in 2003. "Closure" of the ring is impossible. Ashby attributed this "significant error" to "simple-minded use of Einsteinian synchronization" [10]

"Simple-minded" here means *literal*, and what he is telling us is that when the engineers tried to synchronize GPS clocks using Einstein's assumptions, they were unable to do so. Yet the system does (and must) use synchronized clocks, and it does work. So how did they do it?

Earth-Centered Frame Again

Synchronization was achieved by referring clock motion not to "the observer" but to something familiar: the non-rotating, Earth-centered inertial reference frame. The designers of GPS once again abandoned a cardinal rule of relativity and accepted what relativity had forbidden—recourse to a "preferred reference frame." The motion of the clocks was referred to a patch of space with the Earth at its center. They gave up on the idea that whenever a signal source moves in relation to an observer, a different reference frame is created with its very own "time."

"A consistent spacetime coordinate system for a 'patch' that encompasses Earth and its GPS satellites," is considered permissible, Ashby wrote. That way, the system designers did not have to "resort to more than the one such time variable." [11]

This "patch" of non-rotating space is that part of the Earth's gravitational field near the Earth. In the center is the Earth itself, rotating on its axis. Within this "patch," or field, there is a single, unitary time, and all the (corrected) satellite clocks tick at the same rate.

What does "corrected" mean? Two corrections to the clock rates must be applied. They are applied to all the clocks, in the factory, before the clocks are even sent into orbit. The corrections are opposite in sign, and alert readers may well have already guessed what they are.

The first correction must be made because the orbiting clocks, moving at 12,500 miles an hour through the gravitational field, will lose time by comparison with clocks that are stationary within that field. Think of the field as generating resistance to the clock's mechanism as it transits the field at high speed. This slows the clocks down, if only to a small extent

We saw earlier that when "clocks" called mesons move at speed through the gravitational field, they have longer half lives. Their internal clocks tick more slowly. We saw the same thing with the "jet-lagged clocks" of Hafele and Keating. The same was true of radio signals bounced off GPS satellites and around the world. All these results were consistent. Moving clocks really do run slow.

But it's important to realize that this one-time, pre-launch clock correction is not in accordance with Einstein's special theory. That would require a subtly different correction, or rather many corrections. In special relativity, the effect-causing velocity is with respect to the observer. And the observer is whoever is holding a GPS receiver, anywhere on the surface of the Earth.

Consider the orbiting satellites. They are moving at different speeds with respect to that observer, because he is not at the center of the globe. A strictly Einsteinian velocity correction would have to be different at each moment in time, and different for each satellite, because the satellite velocity (with respect to the observer) is continually changing with time. Attempting to enter such constantly changing corrections, depending on the location of tens of thousands of observers spread all over the world, would have made the system unworkable and perhaps logically impossible.

To correct for the motion of the orbiting clocks, therefore, the underlying theory was changed. A single, system-wide clock-rate correction was made. Clock motion was calculated *not* with respect to the observer, but with respect to the non-rotating Earth-centered inertial frame. Since the clocks do all move through this field or patch of space at the same velocity, a single correction was entered.

For practical reasons this was necessary. Clocks orbiting at 12,500 miles an hour in fact lose 7 millionths of a second (relative to Earth clocks) in a day. For clocks continuously in orbit this lag would be cumulative and the whole system would quickly fall out of sync if uncorrected.

A second and larger correction also had to be made, in accordance with general relativity. In the attenuated gravitational field 11,000 miles up, clocks run faster than identical clocks at ground level. As Peter Galison put it, the "weaker gravitational field would leave the satellite clocks running fast (relative to the Earth's surface) by 45 millionths of a second per day."

I discuss the general theory in the following chapters but the argument is that it takes a roundabout route to the right solutions. Accordingly, it is reasonable to call this large GPS correction relativistic. Notice how Galison phrased it, however. Perhaps unconsciously, he said it was the *clocks* (not time) that ran fast, and he was surely right about that.

So the two corrections work in opposite directions. In fact, if the satellites orbited closer to the Earth, at a height of about 1900 miles, the two corrections would cancel each other. As it is, the correction for altitude is over six times larger than that for speed. Add them together and we are left with what Galison called "a staggering correction of 38 millionths (that is 38,000 billionths) of a second per day in a GPS system that had to be accurate to within 50 billionths of a second each day."[12]

The relevant corrections were "10,000 times too large to ignore," Ashby wrote. "If these relativistic effects were not corrected for, satellite clock errors building up in just one day would cause navigational errors of more than 11 kilometers, quickly rendering the system useless."[13]

There is one more correction, making allowance for the Earth's rotation during the signal transmission time. As the signal is *en route*, the observer is moving to the east along a line of latitude. On a much larger scale, it is the same as the Sagnac effect. Visualize it by thinking of the GPS signal as traveling in the gravitational field of the Earth, while the observer on the surface is moving (with the Earth's rotation) through that field as the signal travels to the ground.

The Earth's rotation during transmission also explains the difference between the speed of light, east and west. Obviously, the distance from New York to Rome is the same as it is from Rome to New York. But if the signal from New York is launched into a non-rotating medium, and the Earth meanwhile rotates, then the Earth (and Rome with it) will have rotated to the east, away from the approaching signal. If the signal goes the other way, the Earth (and New York with it) will move toward the arriving signal.

But this simple way of looking at what is going on is closed to the relativists, who made their lives more complicated by postulating a constant light speed. Then they tried to put everything back together again by expanding time and shrinking space as necessary.

At the end of his *Physics Today* article, Neil Ashby comments that although ordinary users of the GPS "may not need to be aware of it," they have in so doing "become dependent on Einstein's conception of space and time."[14] Not really. Certainly Einstein's gravitational correction is in the system, and it wouldn't work without it. But Einstein's conception of time was dropped. GPS was made to work precisely at the cost of abandoning the idea that motion must be referred to the observer. It is referred to the field—a preferred reference frame. "For all their talk, they are adopting Petr Beckmann's reference system," Howard Hayden said.

The relativistic departures from the predictions of classical physics entailed by relativity theory are miniscule. It was only with atomic clocks that those tiny slivers of time could be measured. With GPS, a practical use was then found for the orbiting clocks. At that point Einstein's theory obliged physicists to see if it worked in practice. The gravitational part of the theory worked well. But applied strictly, the special theory entailed hopeless complications and non-synchronizable clocks. Inevitably, they would have rendered the system unworkable. So the special theory was quietly amended, and now GPS runs like clockwork.

Notes Chapter 17

[1]   Peter Galison, *Einstein's Clocks, Poincare's Maps*, W. W. Norton, 2003, p. 287.

[2]   Edwin F. Taylor and John Archibald Wheeler, *Exploring Black Holes, Introduction to General Relativity*, Addison Wesley Longman, 2000, A1

[3]   Neil Ashby, "Relativity and the Global Positioning System," *Physics Today*, May 2002, p. 41.

[4]   Ashby, *Physics Today,* p. 42.

[5]   Sartori, *Understanding Relativity*, p. 62.

[6]   Jeremy Bernstein, *Einstein*, Penguin, p. 63

[7]   Philip Yam, "Everyday Einstein," *Scientific American*, Sept. 2004, p. 55

[8]   Sartori, pp. 60-62.

[9]   N. Ashby, D. W. Allan, M.A. Weiss, "Around-the-World Relativistic Sagnac Experiment," *Science*, 1985, pp. 69-70.

[10] Neil Ashby, "Relativity in the Global Positioning System," *Living Reviews in Relativity*, 28 Jan 2003, p. 9; *Physics Today*, op. cit., p. 47.

[11] Ashby, *Physics Today*, p. 42.

[12] Galison, *Einstein's Clocks*, p. 288.

[13] Ashby, *Physics Today*, p. 41.

[14] Ashby, *Physics Today*, p. 47.

Chapter 18. The General Theory

The Principle of Equivalence

"I was sitting in a chair in the patent office at Bern when all of a sudden a thought occurred to me: 'If a person falls freely he will not feel his own weight.' I was startled. This simple thought made a deep impression on me. It impelled me toward a theory of gravitation."[1]

Einstein later called this his "happiest thought." It pointed toward the solution of his problem: How to generalize his "special" principle of relativity, which applied only to uniform motion.

The passenger who feels a railway carriage suddenly slow down is not compelled to attribute this sensation to a real deceleration. He might also interpret it this way: 'My body of reference (the carriage) remains permanently at rest. With reference to it, however, there exists (during the period of application of the brakes) a gravitational field which is directed forwards and which is variable with respect to time."[2]

Einstein is saying that one who feels an inertial force and attributes it to the slowing train can consider the possibility that he is experiencing a gravitational force acting in the opposite direction. Einstein called this the principle of equivalence. Gravitation and acceleration can have equivalent effects. If we define our reference frame with sufficient care, we can argue that passengers would not be able to tell whether they were being acted upon by gravity or by acceleration.

These undecided observers are often depicted inside an enclosed box in outer space where there is no gravitational field. The box is then accelerated "up," and occupants would have equal reason to think that they were being pressed "down" in a gravitational field. Einstein was the first to publish this thought experiment, just as he was the first to introduce us to "our old friend the railway carriage."[3]

Here's a good exposition by the physicist Lawrence Krauss:

> When you are in an elevator, how do you know when and in what direction it has started to move? Well, if it begins to move upward,

you momentarily feel heavier; if it moves downward, you momentarily feel lighter. But how do you *know* that it is actually moving, and not that gravity has suddenly gotten stronger?

The answer is, you don't. There is not a single experiment you can do in a closed elevator that can tell you whether you are accelerating or in a stronger gravitational field. We can make it even simpler. Put the elevator in empty space, with no Earth around. When the elevator is at rest, or moving at a constant velocity, nothing pulls you toward the floor. If the elevator is accelerating upward, however, the floor must push upward on you with some force to accelerate you along with the elevator. ...

...Einstein realized that the laws of physics are identical for observers moving at a constant acceleration as those in a constant gravitational field. In this way, he argued that even acceleration is relative. One person's acceleration is another's gravity.[4]

Einstein was guided toward the equivalence principle by the fact, supposedly demonstrated at the Leaning Tower of Pisa, that whatever their weight, all objects fall with the same acceleration in a gravitational field. Since the force of attraction between the Earth and objects of different weights must be different, Newton hypothesized that the heavier objects are also held back by an inertial force that is proportional to their weight. Newton confirmed this by timing pendulums of equal length but different weight, showing that their periods were the same.

In 1890, the Hungarian physicist Roland von Eotvos confirmed to a much higher level of accuracy that objects made of different materials have equal inertial and gravitational masses. In 1964, the physicist R. H. Dicke improved on that by a factor of one hundred.[5]

Einstein hypothesized that the two forms of mass were proportional for a simple reason. Gravitational and inertial forces are different manifestations of the same thing. Whether you think you are experiencing one or the other depends on what frame of reference you are assumed to be in—at rest in a gravitational field, or accelerating in a region remote from such a field.

The principle of equivalence became the central postulate of general relativity. Assuming that gravity and acceleration are equivalent, Einstein deduced the consequences. It was a practical idea, in addition to an inspired one. Since accelerating a body is far easier than changing its gravitational field—on the Earth's surface, the field is an inescapable constant—investigation is simplified. If we can calculate what happens in an accelerating body, we can assume by that the same effect will arise in a gravitational field.

Suppose we want to know how the laws of electromagnetism are affected by a strong gravitational field. "A priori, the curious physicists would have to set sail for the nearest black hole" and set up their lab there, the pseudonymous physicist A. Zee wrote. But if Einstein was right, all they had to do was pack their instruments into a box and accelerate it fast enough. In fact, "there is no need to go to all this trouble—the physicists can lie back and simply imagine the whole exercise."[6]

Light Rays in Gravitational Fields

Einstein duly imagined the whole exercise, and in 1911— midway between his special and general theories— published a paper entitled "The Influence of Gravitation on the Propagation of Light." He visualized two reference frames, one in a gravitational field, the other accelerated, and he assumed that they are "physically exactly equivalent."[7]   He deduced two results that can be tested experimentally. One is known as the "gravitational red-shift," and the other is the better known bending of light in a gravitational field.

Consider that we are in an enclosed ship accelerating "upwards" in a remote part of space. There is no gravitational field. Someone within the vehicle sends a beam of light across the interior space. Because the space-ship is accelerating "up," the light beam is seen to curve down a little as it crosses the room. According to the equivalence principle, the physics within the accelerating spaceship and a gravitational field are the same. Ergo, gravity bends light rays.

The gravitational red-shift can be thought of as a direct consequence of the slightly increased speed of a light beam as it moves away from the center of a gravitational mass. In the more rarefied field, it will also have a longer wave length than the same wave at a lower altitude. The case of a light beam heading straight toward or away from the center of a gravitating body (e.g. the Earth) can be thought of as a special case. In the general case the beam (not heading toward the center) will come at an angle through the field and will also be refracted.

Of course, the Einsteinians are hamstrung by their allegiance to special relativity, which decrees a constant light speed, so they are not free to express things so simply. But Einstein did liberate himself in his 1911 paper, Because "the velocity of light in the gravitational field is a function of the place," he wrote, "we may easily infer, by means of Huygens's principle, that light rays propagated across a gravitational field undergo deflection."[8]

Christian Huygens, who proposed that light travels in waves, lived in 17th century Holland and of course knew nothing of relativity. His principle shows how light waves can travel rectilinearly through space. It can also be used to explain the refraction of light at the interface between two media (e.g. air and water) in which light travels at different speeds.

With light either slowed or deflected by gravitational fields— and in a universe with lots of galaxies, gravitational fields are ubiquitous—we should remember that light does not *normally* travel in a straight line, at a constant speed. Again, In Einstein's words:

> [O]ur result shows that, according to the general theory of relativity, the law of the constancy of the velocity of light *in vacuo*, which constitutes one of the two fundamental assumptions in the special theory of relativity . . . cannot claim any unlimited validity. A curvature of rays of light can only take place when the velocity of propagation varies with position. Now we might think that as a consequence of this, the special theory of relativity would be laid in the dust. But in reality this is not the case. We can only conclude that the special theory of relativity cannot claim an unlimited domain of validity; its results hold only so long as we are able to disregard the influence of gravitational fields on the phenomena (*e.g.* of light).[9]

Put briefly, he is saying that light does *not* go at a constant speed as long as we are obliged to take the influence of gravity into account. (But in what location can gravity be disregarded?)

This was not some intermediate position that Einstein later amended. In his paper on general relativity, published in 1916, he again pointed out that in a gravitational field, "the principle of the constancy of the velocity of light *in vacuo* must be modified."[10]

In short, the constancy of the speed of light is valid only as long as we can disregard an influence (gravity) that is present in every earthbound experiment. And what this tells us is that special relativity covers not so much a special as an ideal case.

One consequence is that the Einsteinians have felt free to disqualify experimental outcomes in conflict with special relativity on the grounds that Earth's gravity made itself felt in the particular case. We already saw this with the Sagnac and the Michelson-Gale experiments.

Generalizing a special or an ideal case, as Einstein did in general relativity, may not have been the best way to proceed. In the ideal case light can be thought of as traveling at a constant speed. But in the general case, which in practice applies in every earthbound experiment, light is curved or slowed by gravity and so does not travel at a constant speed.

Howard Hayden was perhaps the first to point out the peculiar order in which Einstein's two theories of relativity were devised. As he put it:

> Einstein recognized that in reality the path of light is curved in a gravitational field. And he also recognized that the speed of light is lower in an intense gravitational field. But he had to operate with the constraints generated by special relativity. One was that the speed of light must be a constant—that he must end up with the same numerical value for c everywhere. The other was that the path of light must be straight, at least locally. In order to find out what happened 1000 meters away from a given position of the light beam, he had to integrate all those values of the changes in the position of the beam.
>
> They arise because the speed of light is not in fact constant and because its path is not in fact straight. So this got him into what they call differential geometry. This complicated general relativity immensely, and unnecessarily. Without special relativity, he could have said that the speed of light varies with the radius, as it demonstrably does; and that the path of light curves, as it demonstrably does. Then he could have produced a much simpler theory of gravity, and one that I think would have produced the same results as Petr Beckmann's theory.[11]

If Einstein had tackled the general theory first, in other words, without being encumbered by the conditions of the special theory, general relativity could have been simplified.

Instead, he added a further complication. He sought to generalize the special case by saying that light does go straight—in four-dimensional space-time. Light rays must now be thought of as traveling along "geodesics." These *look* curved in three dimensions but they take the shortest route in four-dimensional space-time. So they can be thought of as "straight" after all.

"Instead of saying that light rays and shortest distances are curved," George Gamow wrote, "he suggested that space itself (more accurately space-time) is curved." Gamow's further comment was later echoed by Edward Teller (they were friends): "It is difficult to conceive of a curved three-dimensional space, let alone a curved four-dimensional space-time, but some idea of what it means can be gleaned from an analogy with two-dimensional surfaces."[12]

That analogy is found in the relationship between a spherical globe and a flat map. The shortest route by plane from London to Washington is a great circle that goes far to the north. Project that route onto a two-dimensional map and it will appear as a curve. On the three dimensional globe, however, the great circle route will be a segment of the earth's circumference that, if extended, passes through the center of the earth; on a globe it will look "straight." Lines that are curved on a flat, two dimensional map look straight on a three dimensional globe, in other words. Add a dimension, then, and curved looks straight.

But notice how Martin Gardner explains Einstein's maneuver:

> When you read about the 'bending' of light by gravity or inertia, you must remember that this is just a three-dimensional way of speaking. In space, the light does indeed curve. But in four-dimensional space-time, light continues, as in classical physics, to move along geodesics. It takes the 'straightest' possible path.[13]

Gardner derogates what is "just" a three-dimensional way of speaking. But that is the way we normally do speak about three-dimensional space. Adding a fourth dimension may have helped to preserve the decorum of special relativity, but without it everything could have been much simpler.

The question is: Do we need relativity, special or general, to explain the effects of gravity? Famously, Einstein justified his general theory (and became world-renowned) by predicting that light would bend slightly in a gravitational field. But this can be explained in more simply once we reject the claim that light travels at a constant velocity. So is relativity theory necessary?

Notes Chapter 18

[1]   Einstein, Talk in Kyoto, Dec 14, 1922. See *Science*, March 5, 1999.
[2]   Einstein, *The Special and General Theory,* p. 70.
[3]   Einstein, *The Special and General Theory*, p. 16.
[4]   Lawrence M. Krauss, *Fear of Physics*, Jonathan Cape, 1994, p. 123.
[5]   R. H. Dicke, *Scientific American*, December 1961.
[6]   A. Zee, *An Old Man's Toy, Gravity at Work and Play in Einstein's Universe*, Macmillan, 1989, p. 20.
[7]   *The Principle of Relativity*, p. 100.
[8]   *The Principle of Relativity*, p. 107.
[9]   Einstein, *The Special and General Theory*, p. 76.
[10] *The Principle of Relativity*, p. 114.
[11] Howard Hayden, author's interview, 2004.
[12] George Gamow, "Gravity," *Scientific American*, March 1961, p. 99.
[13] Martin Gardner, *Relativity Simply Explained*, Dover, 1997, p. 95.

Chapter 19. Bending of Light Rays

General relativity should meet three tests, Einstein said. His first and most famous prediction was that light rays passing by the Sun would be deflected. The second was not really a prediction because it was already known: the orbit of Mercury deviated from the prediction of Newtonian theory. The third, proposed by Einstein as early as 1907, predicted a gravitational "red-shift" of light. Its wave-length would increase as it moved out to a more attenuated gravitational field.[1]

Confirmation of Einstein's first prediction turned him into a world famous figure. The key was that it could be understood by laymen. Paul Johnson wrote in the opening paragraph of *Modern Times* that the "modern world began on 29 May 1919 when photographs of a solar eclipse, taken off the island of Principe off West Africa and at Sobral in Brazil, confirmed the truth of a new theory of the universe."[2]

An expedition to the Crimea to observe an earlier eclipse, in 1914, led by Einstein's friend Erwin Freundlich, was stymied by war, so 1919 was the first post-war opportunity. One expedition was led by the British astronomer Arthur Eddington. The London *Times* published his early findings under the headline: "Revolution in Science. New Theory of the Universe. Newtonian Ideas Overthrown." Two days later, the *New York Times* proclaimed: "Lights all askew in the heavens / Men of science more or less agog over the eclipse observation / Einstein theory triumphs."[3]

From that point on, Paul Johnson continued, "Einstein was a global hero, in demand at every great university in the world, mobbed wherever he went, his wistful features familiar to hundreds of millions, the archetype of the abstracted natural philosopher."[4]

The anomaly of Mercury's orbit, known by the mid 19th century, was not so much a prediction as a problem to be resolved. By 1907, when Einstein was working on a new theory of gravitation, he told a friend he hoped to explain Mercury's "anomalous precession with its help."[5] (See chapter 20.)

More recent results have further confirmed the general theory. One test was proposed by Irwin Shapiro of MIT and confirmed in 1969. Radar signals passing close to the Sun and reflected from

Venus should take a little excess time—the time delay—compared to the normal travel time. And in the late 1970s it was shown that light from distant galaxies is "bent" around intervening dark matter, forming rings or brighter images in the telescope.

Bending of starlight in a gravitational field

In Book 3 of the *Opticks*, published in 1704, Isaac Newton proposed some Queries as an addition to his work on Optics, one of which asked: "Do not Bodies act upon Light at a distance, and by their action bend its Rays...?"[6]

In 1801 the German astronomer Johann Georg von Soldner, "became the first to answer Newton's query on the bending of light," Abraham Pais wrote. Soldner's calculations, based on Newton's particle theory of light, predicted that light rays near the sun would be bent by 0.84 seconds of arc.[7] In 1911, Einstein calculated the deflection of starlight using his equivalence principle. He came up with a deflection of 0.83 seconds of arc, essentially the same as Soldner's.[8] Four years later, however, Einstein recalculated the deflection using general relativity and came up with a deflection twice as great—about 1.7 seconds of arc.[9] Modern measurements of the deflection are much closer to the latter figure.

General relativity gave an answer closely corresponding to the facts, but by a complicated method. For wave fronts do indeed bend in a non-uniform medium. If the local gravitational field is the luminiferous ether, that field is non-uniform. As light from the star enters the denser field near the sun, the light ray bends according to well established principles of refraction. The extent to which it bends depends upon the index of refraction of the medium.

In 1968, Frank R. Tangherlini published an article in the *American Journal of Physics*, arguing that a correct value for the gravitational deflection of light could be calculated without general relativity by using Snell's Law, formulated in the 17th century. When a light ray enters a denser medium it is refracted at a certain angle. Snell's Law demonstrates mathematically how the change in angle is related to the change of velocity. In the same way, when the starlight enters the denser gravitational field of the Sun, it bends and slows down. Tangherlini showed that these calculations could be used to give exactly the formula that Einstein used for the refraction.[10]

But this simplified line of reasoning was not available to Einstein who had eliminated the light medium. Tangherlini cited several authors who had made arguments similar to his own, among them Leonard Schiff, then chairman of the Stanford physics department. Schiff was one of the originators of the Gravity Probe B experiment, a test of general relativity in space that was finally launched in 2004.

Over 20 years later, a different approach was made by two Chinese physicists, Renhe Tian and Zhuhuai Li. In a paper, published by the *American Journal of Physics* in 1990, they derived the speed and apparent rest mass of a photon in a gravitational field. Using classical principles, including the conservation of energy and angular momentum, they calculated the deflection of starlight. They found that it gave "a correct amount of the angular deflection . . . which is the same as that given by general relativity theory." They added that "many authors have presented the same results," using different approaches.[11]

Six months earlier, Howard Hayden had arrived at the same result in a paper published by *Galilean Electrodynamics*. He calculated the deflection of starlight by integrating the deflections due both to the impulse from the gravitational attraction and from the varying index of refraction of the progressively denser field. For light grazing the sun, the result was "in agreement with experiment and with General Relativity Theory." In his conclusion Hayden wrote:

> The deflection of starlight by the sun was measured in 1919 as a check on general relativity theory (GRT). The agreement thus obtained was heralded as support for GRT; 'curved spacetime' has since become part of the literature. The problem solved by GRT was, however, one created by special relativity theory in assuming that the speed of light is constant. We show here that the 'curved spacetime' invention is totally unnecessary for the calculation of the deflection of starlight. The identical result can be had with a few lines of high school algebra and a couple of trivial integrals, using Newtonian time and Euclidian geometry.[12]

In the same issue, Petr Beckmann published a one-page paper showing that the optical part of the trajectory of light in a gravitational field could be derived from Hayden's formula for the refractive index, and from Fermat's principle. Formulated in the 17th century by the French mathematician Pierre de Fermat, this says that light propagates along a path that minimizes the time interval for propagation between two points. Beckmann wrote in his final paragraph:

> The total bending angle, which at present is the only measurable quantity, agrees with the Einstein theory; the light trajectory is slightly different. Its derivation is not only far simpler than that by Einstein's General Theory, but within Fermat's principle (geometric optics) it is exact, whereas the Einsteinian trajectory is found under the assumptions of the General Einstein Theory by successive approximations of the resulting differential equation.[13]

As early as 1920, Arthur Eddington had also shown how the observed result could be derived using classical physics. He compared the wave motion of light to sea waves approaching a beach. If one end of the wave reaches shallow water before the other, the speed of the wave will be reduced, and "the whole wave front must gradually slew around, and the direction in which it is rolling must change." In the same way, he added, "when the light waves pass near the sun, the end nearest the sun has the smaller velocity and the wave-front slews round."

> Light moves more slowly in a material medium than in vacuum, the velocity being inversely proportional to the refractive index of the medium. The phenomenon of refraction is in fact caused by a slewing of the wave-front in passing into a region of smaller velocity. We can thus imitate the gravitational effect precisely, if we imagine the space round the sun filled with a refractive medium which gives the appropriate velocity of light. . . . Any problem on the paths of rays near the sun can now be solved by the method of geometric optics applied to the equivalent refractive medium.[14]

Admittedly, Eddington posits a refractive medium with the value that "gives the appropriate velocity of light," but the Chinese physicists above had done that using only the conservation of energy and of angular momentum—physical principles that long precede relativity theory.

Gravitational Red-shift

Einstein first predicted this effect in 1907, when he said that a "clock, and, more generally, any physical process," would proceed faster "the greater the gravitational potential." To clarify, a point high above the Earth has a greater gravitational potential than one at lower altitude. Therefore, clocks in space tick faster than close-in clocks. Einstein then reinterpreted this in terms of the increased wave-length of light moving from the gravitational field of the sun to that of the Earth.[15] He restated the argument in his 1911 paper, as we saw in the previous chapter.

The gravitational red-shift, not to be confused with the better known cosmological red-shift caused by the mutual recession of galaxies, is simply the prediction that a light ray moving up or down in a gravitational field, will produce a small shift in its wave length and frequency. Another way of putting it is to say that clocks slow down, and light rays slow down, as they enter the denser field.

The red-shift is so small in the terrestrial field that detection for a long time was not thought feasible. Then it was found that gamma rays are emitted at precise frequencies in the radioactive decay of certain isotopes. A receiver can be stationed so that it absorbs these rays, and if the receiver is vertically above or below the emitter, then (according to the Einstein prediction) there will be a small frequency shift as these rays move into the different field. Then receiver and emitter will no longer be "in resonance."

The technical difficulty that these experiments encountered was that the atomic nuclei "tend to jiggle around," as Jeremy Bernstein wrote, "and this jiggling leads to a lack of precision in defining the light frequency." But in 1958 R. L. Mossbauer found a way of embedding the nuclei in crystals, and that stopped the jiggling.[16] The expected shift in frequency was confirmed by R. V. Pound and Glen A. Rebka at Harvard in 1960. Rays were allowed to fall vertically through a mere 74 feet. Using the Mossbauer effect, they were able to detect a frequency shift of one part in ten to the fifteenth power. Mossbauer received the Nobel Prize in 1961.

In his analysis, Petr Beckmann wrote that the experiments confirmed the prediction of the Einstein theory. And "this was regarded as another confirmation of the theory." But, Beckmann added,

> the behavior of electromagnetic waves in a gravitational field must of necessity depend on their velocity of propagation as a function of the field intensity, or to use optical terminology, on the refractive index of a gravitational field. This is the case, as it must be, for Einstein's theory of gravitation, but the corresponding function is arrived at by a physically opaque matrix calculus in non-Euclidean

space. On the other hand, for a theory based on the fundamental assumption that the velocity of light is constant with respect to the gravitational field through which it propagates, the corresponding index of refraction is the first thing the theory must quite naturally ask for and measure... [17]

Leonard Schiff questioned whether Einstein's general theory was needed to explain red-shift. It is possible to obtain it "in a valid manner without using the full [general] theory," he wrote.[18] A year later, in *Physics Today*, he reported on a NASA conference held at Stanford in 1961 for those interested in the use of orbiting satellites to test relativity. Schiff reported comments of the conference chairman, Caltech's H. P. Robertson:

He then reviewed the present experimental basis of general relativity: the red-shift follows from more elementary considerations and is not really a test of general relativity, and the deflection of light by the sun has not been measured with great precision. Only the precession of the perihelion of the orbit of the planet Mercury provides an accurate test of Einstein's theory.[19]

Shapiro Time Delay

In 1959 it was shown that radar signals could be bounced back from Venus and the echo detected. Improved radar antennae in the next few years made it possible to detect radar echoes from Mercury and Venus when they were on the opposite side of the Sun. Since the orbits of those planets were by then precisely known, calculating how long the round trip should take was an easy matter. (Radar beams are electromagnetic waves with a wave-length longer than that of light but the same speed.)

Irwin Shapiro, then at MIT, calculated that according to general relativity, the echo should return with a small delay if the signal went close by the Sun. In 1964 he submitted a paper to *Physical Review Letters*, outlining this "Fourth Test of General Relativity." It was published at the end of that year, and today the effect is known as the Shapiro time delay. It is very small—250 millionths of a second.

The first test involved bouncing radar beams off Mercury and Venus in 1967. Approximate agreement with theory was found. But there was some uncertainty about the point of reflection from the irregular planet surfaces. Later tests bounced signals off two

Mariner spacecraft, then in approximately the same orbit as Mars. Still later tests, using the Viking spacecraft that landed on Mars in 1976, confirmed the theory with an accuracy of 0.1 percent. It is "still the most accurate test of the theory ever performed," according to Clifford Will.[20]

Shapiro had attended an MIT lecture on measurements of the speed of light in 1961. In passing, the speaker mentioned that "according to general relativity, the speed of light is not constant." This puzzled Shapiro "because he had always thought that according to relativity, the speed of light should be the same in every inertial frame," Will wrote. Shapiro knew that light was deflected by gravitating bodies, but did this mean the speed was affected? It seemed plausible, because in a glass prism, as Will informs us, "the deflection of light as it passes through the prism is a consequence of the change in speed of the light as it passes from air to glass and from glass to air. The two phenomena, change in speed and deflection, appear to be closely related."[21] Eddington had made the same point in 1920. Shapiro consulted Eddington's textbook, and found that according to the equations of the full general theory, "the effective speed of light should indeed vary."

But wasn't light always supposed to have the same speed? Clifford Will, a high priest of relativity today, adjudicates the issue in this fashion. "Whether or not the observer uses the words 'light slows down near the Sun' is purely a question of semantics," he writes. Because the observer "never goes near the Sun to make the measurement, he can't really make such a judgment." All he can say "with no fear of contradiction is that he observed a time delay that depended on how close the light came to the Sun. The only sense in which it can be said that the light slowed down is mathematical."[22]

But speed is always calculated as the ratio of distance and time, and the only sense in which it could *not* be said that the light slowed is also mathematical. Einstein's complex math of four-dimensional space-time gives us the right answer. So does the simpler math of Fermat and Euclid.

The argument here is that in science the simpler should be preferred to the complex, as long as both are consistent with observation.

Relativistically Incorrect

In a way, the most dramatic confirmation of the bending of starlight came with the observation of gravitational lensing. It occurs when a large but distant mass, such as "dark matter," or a galaxy, is directly in the line of sight between an even more distant quasi-stellar object, or quasar, and the telescope. The intervening matter acts as a lens, and light from the more distant object bends around it. It may appear in double or quadruple images (an "Einstein cross"), as a ring, or as thin arcs of light. Einstein mentioned the possibility of gravitational lensing in *Science* magazine as early as 1936.[23]

A year later Fritz Zwicky of Caltech pointed out that galaxies were more likely than stars to act as lenses, and one might even be able to use the effect as a natural telescope. The distant star would be amplified because light from it that would normally have missed the earth is bent by gravity toward the observer. Gravitational lensing was observed for the first time in 1979, when a quasar was observed in a double image.[24]

Since then, "micro-lensing" has become a method of looking for the dark matter that cosmologists believe is out there. The idea is that an abrupt increase in the brightness of a star indicates that dark matter, maybe a "brown dwarf" star, is passing in front of the more distant star. Hundreds of such events have been reported; typically they last from 15 to 90 days.

In short, the idea that light rays bend in the proximity of large masses has been well confirmed. But notice how we talk about these findings. Do large masses "curve" the four-dimensional structure of spacetime? Or does light slow down when it penetrates a gravitational field? And bend according to well established principles of refraction? Discussing this in *Simply Einstein,* Richard Wolfson makes a revealing comment:

> In describing gravitational lenses, I've been using language like 'light bends' and 'focusing of light by gravity.' That language helps explain the phenomenon, but it isn't quite relativistically correct. What's actually happening, of course, is that light is going in the straightest possible lines in curved spacetime. It's just that those aren't the ideal straight lines of tenth-grade geometry. Sometimes— as when multiple images form—the geometry of spacetime is such that there's more than one 'straightest line' between a distant object and Earth.[25]

The subtitle of Wolfson's book is "Relativity Demystified." But his commitment to Einstein's theory forces him to reject simplicity because it isn't "relativistically correct." We might prefer to think of things this way: "What's actually happening" (to use Wolfson's words) is that light *really is* curving—in three-dimensional space. Maybe Einsteinians really would like to demystify their subject, but their adherence to the doctrines of special relativity forces them to discuss gravitational fields in a difficult way.

Notes: Chapter 19

[1] A. Einstein, (1907) *The Collected Papers of Albert Einstein*, vol. 2, Princeton, 1989, p. 307.

[2] Paul Johnson, *Modern Times,* revised edition, 1991, New York HarperCollins, p. 1.

[3] *The Times* (London), November 7, 1919; *New York Times*, November 9, 1919. See A. Pais, *'Subtle is the Lord'* ..., chap. 16.

[4] Paul Johnson, op. cit., p. 3.

[5] John Stachel, *From 'B' to 'Z'*, p. 235.

[6] Sir Isaac Newton, *Opticks*, based on 4th edition, London 1730, preface by I. Bernard Cohen, Dover, 1952, p. 339.

[7] Abraham Pais, *'Subtle is the Lord'* ... p. 200.

[8] Pais, op. cit., p. 199, 200.

[9] Pais, op. cit., p. 255.

[10] Frank R. Tangherlini, "On Snell's Law and the Gravitational Deflection of Light," *Am. J. Physics*, Nov 1968, p. 1001-04.

[11] Renhe Tian and Zhuhuai Li, "The speed and apparent rest mass of photons in a gravitational field," *American Journal of Physics*, Sept 1990, pp. 890-92.

[12] Howard Hayden, "Light Speed as a Function of Gravitational Potential," *Galilean Electrodynamics*, vol 1, March/April 1990, pp. 15-17.

[13] Petr Beckmann, "Light Path in a Gravitational Field by Hayden's Formula and Fermat's Principle," *Galilean Electrodynamics*, vol 1, March/April 1990, p. 18.

[14] Sir Arthur Eddington, *Space, Time and Gravitation*, Cambridge University Press, 1920, Harper Torchbooks, 1959, pp. 108-09.

[15] Einstein, *Collected Papers*, vol. 2, p. 307.

[16] Jeremy Bernstein, *Einstein*, p. 152.

[17] Petr Beckmann, *Einstein Plus Two*, p. 99.

[18] L. I. Schiff, "On Experimental Tests of the General Theory of Relativity," *American Journal of Physics*, 28 (1960), p. 340.

[19] L. I. Schiff, "Experimental Tests of Theories of Relativity," *Physics Today*, 14, p. 42.
[20] Clifford M. Will, *Was Einstein Right*, p. 134.
[21] Will, op. cit., p. 110, 111.
[22] Will, op. cit., p. 113.
[23] A. Einstein, "Lens like action of a star by the deviation of light in the gravitational field," *Science*, 84, (1936), p. 506.
[24] Joachim Wambsganss, "Gravitational Lensing in Astronomy," *Living Reviews of Relativity*, 1, (1998), 12 (online article, cited April 2004).
[25] Wolfson, *Simply Einstein: Relativity Demystified*, Norton, 2003, p. 214.

Chapter 20. Mercury's Orbit

According to Newton's theory of gravitation, the orbit of a planet is an ellipse with the sun at one focus. The observed motions are slightly more complicated because the various planets also feel the gravitational attraction of each other. In the 18th century, Newtonian mechanics explained these perturbations to a high degree of accuracy. Only in the case of Mercury was there a small inaccuracy. Its perihelion—the point where its orbit comes closest to the sun—advances by a small amount each year. It is not a closed ellipse, always repeating the same path. Newton's theory had predicted a perihelion advance, but a discrepancy of 43 seconds of arc per century remained.

It is impressive that so small an anomaly was observed in the mid 19th century. Joseph LeVerrier submitted his discovery to the Academy of Sciences in Paris, in 1859. The unexpected advance in the perihelion was due to "some as yet unknown action on which no light has been thrown," he wrote. It was "worthy of attention by astronomers." Among the possibilities was an underestimate of Venus's mass, or an undetected Mercurial moon.

A small departure from Newton's inverse square law would perturb planetary orbits, so that was considered too. But "these attempts either failed or are uninteresting because they involved adjustable parameters," Pais wrote. The value of 43 seconds of arc, given by Simon Newcomb in 1882, did not change over the next hundred years.[1]

Einstein was aware of the problem. In 1907 he told Conrad Habicht that he was examining the law of gravitation, "by which I hope to be able to explain the hitherto unexplained secular changes in the perihelion distance of Mercury."[2] Albrecht Folsing refers to it as "the only flaw which astronomers had established in the Newtonian world picture."

In November 1915 Einstein presented his solution to the Prussian Academy. Mercury's orbit was explained by his general theory "without any special hypothesis having to be postulated for it." He told the physicist Arnold Sommerfeld that the result filled him "with great satisfaction" and was amused that he was now advocating the very "pedantic accuracy of astronomy that I often made quiet fun of in the past!"[3]

Pais believed that this was "by far the strongest emotional experience in Einstein's scientific life, perhaps in all his life. Nature had spoken to him."[4] Einstein told friends that it had given him heart palpitations. When he saw his calculations agreed with the unexplained observation, "he had the feeling that something actually snapped in him."

Then controversy erupted. The formula accounting for Mercury's orbit had already been published. In 1898, seventeen years before the general theory was completed, a man named Paul Gerber published Einstein's formula in the journal *Zeitschrift fur Mathematik und Physik*. His calculations assumed that gravity propagates with some finite speed; he based his derivation of his equation on the known value for the precession of Mercury's orbit, concluding that gravity travels at the speed of light.[5]

In 1902, a longer version of his article was published as a report by the high school where Gerber taught at the turn of the century.

Petr Beckmann was in Boulder writing *Einstein Plus Two* when a correspondent in England sent him the reference to Gerber's article. He immediately bicycled to the University of Colorado library and could hardly believe his eyes when he saw it. In *Einstein Plus Two* Beckmann included a photograph of Gerber's page showing the formula; the same as Einstein's.

Beckmann tried to find out more, but the trail was cold. Gerber died before Einstein's general theory was published. He "appears to have been a high school science teacher in the little German town of Stargard, Pomerania," Beckmann wrote. It "was virtually obliterated in World War II, so it may be difficult to find out more about the man who discovered the mechanism turning Mercury's orbit."[6]

In 1916, a physicist named Ernst Gehrcke published an article in *Annalen der Physik* pointing out Gerber's priority.[7] A senior official at the Physical-Technical Reich Institute, Gehrcke was the inventor of various techniques used in spectroscopy.[8] His article was both petulant and vainglorious, claiming an implausible priority for himself in various matters. He went further and implied that Einstein had plagiarized the finding from Gerber. He wrote of the identical but very differently derived equations:

> We might think that this is an amazing coincidence, and that Einstein obtained the same result without any foreknowledge of Gerber's

work. This assumption loses credibility when we learn that Gerber's treatise on the subject is discussed in the well-known *Mechanics* of Mach, and that Einstein displayed a thorough familiarity with this work on the occasion of a memorial address in honor of Mach. Moreover, Gerber's work was also occasionally mentioned in contemporary periodicals...[9]

In 1917, the Annalen editors responded by reprinting in *Annalen der Physik* the longer version of Gerber's article.[10] In *The Science of Mechanics*, which Einstein certainly studied (and praised), Ernst Mach had written:

> Drude (in his report on actions at a distance made for the German Naturforscherversammlung of 1897) enumerated many experiments for establishing a velocity of propagation for gravitation, which go back as far as Laplace. The result is to be regarded as a negative one, for the velocities which are possible to be considered as such, do not accord with one another, though they are all very large multiples of the velocity of light. Paul Gerber alone ("Ueber die raumliche u. zeitliche Ausbreitung der Gravitation," Zeitschrift f. Math. u. Phys. 1898, II), from the perihelial motion of Mercury, forty-one seconds in a century, finds the velocity of propagation of gravitation to be the same as that of light. This would speak in favor of the ether as the medium of gravitation.

Nine German editions of Mach's book were published in his lifetime, the last in 1912. Ernst Gehrcke cited the 1904 edition.[11]

How did Einstein respond? In October 1916 he wrote to a friend that he "would not reply to Gehrcke's tasteless and superficial attacks."[12] But he did reply, in print in 1918, and again in the *Berliner Tageblatt* in August, 1920:

> Mr. Gehrcke wants to give the impression that the perihelion motion of Mercury can also be explained without the theory of relativity. There exist two possibilities.   Either you invent particular interplanetary masses, which are so large and distributed as to give a perihelion motion of the observed amount (that is, of course, an extremely unsatisfactory way compared with the one given by the theory of relativity which yields the perihelion motion of Mercury without any special assumptions); or you use the work of Gerber, who has given the correct formula for the perihelion motion of Mercury before I did. The experts are not only in agreement that Gerber's derivation is wrong through and through, but the formula cannot be obtained as a consequence of the main assumption made

by Gerber. Mr. Gerber's work is therefore completely useless, an unsuccessful and erroneous theoretical attempt.

I maintain that the theory of general relativity has provided the first real explanation of the perihelion motion of Mercury. I have not mentioned the work by Gerber originally, because I did not know it when I wrote my work on the perihelion motion of Mercury; even if I had been aware of it, I would not have had any reason to mention it.[13]

The experts mentioned by Einstein included Max von Laue, a strong Einstein supporter, the astronomer Hugo von Seeliger and the mathematician Wolfgang Pauli. Pauli's book, *Theory of Relativity,* first published in 1921, gives citations to the full discussion of Gerber's article in *Annalen der Physik*. As far as I know, the articles cited by Pauli have not yet been published in English.

In summary, Pauli wrote: "Recently, an earlier attempt by P. Gerber has been discussed which tries to explain the perihelion advance of Mercury with the help of the finite velocity of propagation of gravitation, but which must be considered completely unsuccessful from a theoretical point of view." It "leads admittedly to the correct formula—though on the basis of false deductions."[14]

Pomeranian Schoolmaster

Albrecht Folsing scoffs at the idea that there is a legitimate, non-relativistic derivation of Einstein's formula and he dismisses Gerber's work as the efforts of "the Pomeranian schoolmaster." Von Seeliger pointed out that Gerber "copied things which had long been known to every worker in the field, and that his so-called explanation was based on a crude mathematical mistake."[15]

Still, we may wonder: How did this "crude mathematical mistake," this "completely useless," "unsuccessful and erroneous theoretical attempt," which was "wrong through and through," lead to the formula which, seventeen years later, gave Einstein heart palpitations?

Petr Beckmann took the "long and arduous road" followed by Gerber, and devoted four pages of his own book to doing the calculations by a different method. He used a method for calculating "the simple and general formula for the advance in central motion with a perturbed Newtonian potential" that in 1915 "was not known," but would have made the calculation easier for everyone.

Beckmann discusses the Lagrange function and the Landau-Lifshitz formula, which are advanced but standard mathematics. One can only marvel at the level attained by German high schools in 1898. In the end Beckmann believed he had shown that "the propagation of force with a finite velocity" gave a result that was the same in Gerber's case as in Einstein's. But Gerber had done so "by classical physics based on hard physical concepts"; Einstein "after the abstract acrobatics of curved space-time in the intangible Temple of Tensors."[16]

Now comes a further difficulty, and a point for the Einsteinians:

J. Christopher Clemens, an associate professor of astrophysics at the University of North Carolina, has studied Beckmann's alternative derivation, and concluded that it is erroneous.[17] (He does not claim that Gerber's own derivation was necessarily wrong.) Howard Hayden subsequently studied Beckmann's disputed derivation, and found that the intermediate result in question merely contained a misprint, a missing superscript of 2.

Howard Hayden says that Gerber's paper "basically posits a velocity-dependent potential energy," from which the precession formula could easily be derived. "All of the argument pertains to whether Gerber got the potential energy correct," he says.

Speed of Gravity

In popular books about relativity, little is said about the propagation speed of gravity. It's of interest for there is some uneasiness about the whole subject. Gerber's derivation of the formula for Mercury's orbit brings it to the fore.

In Newton's theory, gravity is assumed to propagate instantaneously. But this seems to imply "action at a distance," a source of discomfort to Newton. He said as much in his famous letter to Richard Bentley—a theologian at Cambridge who shared his heretical religious views.[18] Arthur Eddington described the underlying problem.

[I]s the force of gravitation propagated instantaneously, or with the velocity of light, or some other velocity? Until comparatively recently it was thought that conclusive proof had been given that the speed of gravitation must be far higher than that of light. The argument was something like this. If the Sun attracts Jupiter towards its present position, and Jupiter attracts the Sun towards its present position, the two forces are in the same line and balance. But if the Sun attracts Jupiter towards its previous position and Jupiter attracts the Sun towards its previous position, when the force of attraction started out to cross the gulf, then the two forces give a couple. This couple will tend to increase the angular momentum of the system, and, acting cumulatively, will soon cause an appreciable change of period, disagreeing with observation if the speed is at all comparable with that of light.[19]

A couple is a pair of opposing forces operating in parallel but not in the same line. The force of gravity, arriving with a delay, will tend to pull the planet forward, not just "in" toward the Sun. A component of the force will pull the planet in the direction of its orbital motion. Then it will gain energy, and move out to a greater orbit. The same will happen to all the planets. By the time the sun's "pull" reaches the Earth, and the earth's reaches the Sun, if gravity's speed-limit is that of light, both bodies will have "moved on" for another 8.3 minutes (the time of light travel between them).

The effect, in one calculation, would be to double the earth's distance from the Sun in 1200 years. Obviously this is not happening. So the stability of planetary orbits seems to tell us that gravity must propagate much faster than light. Newton accepted the argument, and was compelled to accept that the force of gravity is instantaneous, perhaps implying "action at a distance."

For this reason, the late astronomer Tom Van Flandern (among others) believed that Paul Gerber's derivation was incorrect. The speed of gravity must be twenty billion times faster than light to sustain stable planetary orbits, he believes. The formula Gerber derived is well known in celestial mechanics. So (Van Flandern argued) the formula could have been a "target" for calculations intended to arrive at just that outcome.

Van Flandern, who worked for the U. S. Naval Observatory in Washington D.C., was a "dissident" theorist. He did not accept relativity, and his *Meta Research Bulletin* espoused sometimes outlandish ideas—notably that artificial features are found on Mars. He published papers about the need to "repeal the speed limit" for gravity in non-dissident journals, one co-authored by Jean-Pierre Vigier of the University of Paris.[20] If Van Flandern is right, then, he "rescues" Einstein from Gerber, but in insisting that the force of gravity travels much faster than light, he creates a greater difficulty.

What does general relativity have to say about the speed of gravity? It sidesteps the whole issue. It is not regarded as a "force" that propagates at all. It is a distortion in the fabric of space-time. It doesn't "go" anywhere. It already *is*, in the non-flat shape of space-time. It is what large objects do to space-time. Gravity *waves*, on the other hand, do travel. They are said to be "ripples" in the fabric of space-time, observing the approved speed limit for light. The only problem is that they haven't been detected yet.

As to the requirement that gravity must be instantaneous or nearly so, in view of stable planetary orbits, Eddington regarded the argument as "fallacious." The effect "will not necessarily be" that the Sun and Jupiter are attracted toward each other's previous position. Indeed, if we substitute electric charges for planets, we find that they are attracted toward each other's actual position, in spite of "the electric influence being propagated with the velocity of light." In the theory given in his own book, Eddington firmly states that "gravitation is propagated with the speed of light."[21]

Howard Hayden tentatively sides with Gerber, and Eddington. "I think we have pretty good proof that electric and magnetic fields propagate with the speed of light," he says today. Van Flandern's argument "should apply equally well to the hydrogen atom. The electron should escape, and probably in rather short order. It doesn't do so."[22]

What is the conclusion? Newton's law of gravitation, having triumphed for 200 years, broke down in one or two particulars. General relativity was said to have succeeded where Newtonian physics failed. But the bending of starlight can be accounted for without Einstein, and so can the gravitational red-shift.

Mercury's orbit departed from the Newtonian schedule by 43 seconds of arc in a century. But 18 years before Einstein's theory was invented, his formula for Mercury's orbit was derived without relativity. Perhaps Gerber's calculations add up, perhaps not. Perhaps Beckmann's recalculation is fatally flawed, perhaps not. Adjudicating a dispute that most physicists have not even heard of is way above my pay grade.

A website called MathPages has reviewed the matter. The article, "Gerber's Gravity," seems even-handed. The author or authors find support "for the complaints of previous reviewers," who characterized Gerber's paper as "unintelligible," "incorrect" and so on. They also conclude "with a speculative re-construction of a classical line of reasoning that Gerber might have used to justify his potential, if he had thought of it and/or been able to express it intelligibly."[23]

The question of Mercury's orbit needs a dispassionate review. Most papers on the subject, including Gerber's, have not yet been published in English. Most laymen *and* physicists have not even heard of the controversy. Let us hope that others will re-examine it.

Notes: Chapter 20

[1] Abraham Pais, *'Subtle is the Lord'* ... pp. 253-54.

[2] Albrecht Folsing, *Albert Einstein, A Biography*, Viking, 1997, p. 306.

[3] Folsing, op. cit., p. 373.

[4] Pais, op. cit., p. 253.

[5] P. Gerber, *Zeitschrift fur Mathematik und Physik*, v. 43, 1898, pp. 93-104.

[6] Petr Beckmann, *Einstein Plus Two*, p. 171.

[7] E. Gehrcke, "Critique and history of the most recent theories of gravitation," *Annalen der Physik*, 51, 1916, pp. 119-124.

[8] Folsing op. cit., p. 461.

[9] Gehrcke, op. cit., p. 124. Translation for author by The Polyglot Shop.

[10] Paul Gerber, "The Propagation Speed of Gravity," *Annalen der Physik*, 1917, pp. 415-444.

[11] Ernst Mach, *The Science of Mechanics*, Open Court, 1960, pp. 234-235.

[12] Folsing, op. cit., p. 461.

[13] Albert Einstein, August 27, 1920, in *Albert Einstein's Theory of General Relativity*, ed. Gerald E. Tauber, Crown, 1979, p. 98.

[14] W. Pauli, *Theory of Relativity*, Dover, p. 169.

[15] Folsing, op. cit., p. 462.

[16] Beckmann, op. cit., pp. 172-175.

[17] J. Christopher Clemens, emails to author, February 2007.

[18] Newton letter to Richard Bentley, 25 Feb 1693. (Available online.)

[19] Arthur Eddington, *Space, Time and Gravitation*, 1920, p. 94.

[20] Tom Van Flandern, "The Speed of Gravity – What the Experiments Say," *Physics Letters A*, v 250, (1998), 1-11; "Reply to Comment on 'The Speed of Gravity,' *Physics Letters A*, v. 262 (1999), pp. 261-263.

[21] Eddington, op. cit., p. 94.

[22] Howard Hayden, e-mail to author, April 2004.

[23] www.mathpages.com/home/kmath525

Chapter 21. Einstein's New Ether

Einstein's rejection of the classical ether in 1905 received a lot of attention, but his revival of a different ether in 1916 received almost no attention. Few authors of popular works know about it. Walter Isaacson, who discussed it in his best-selling biography, *Einstein: His Life and Universe,* was a notable exception.

The topic is reviewed in Ludwik Kostro's *Einstein and the Ether,* the first book on the subject. In a foreword, Max Jammer says that the term ether "is unique in the history of physics ... because it is the only term that has been eliminated and subsequently reinstated, though with a different connotation, by one and the same physicist."[1]

In a semi-laudatory review of Kostro's book, John Stachel said that it was "well worth reading," but he also criticized the author, a Polish philosopher of science, for shunning insight in favor of "long undigested passages from the original papers."[2] But original quotations are often valuable, especially when we have not seen them before, so I shall quote one or two of them myself.

Sir Arthur Eddington also reintroduced an ether, and in 1951 Paul Dirac said we can see "that we may very well have an aether, subject to quantum mechanics and conforming to relativity."[3]

Einstein's revival of a new ether is of great interest because in conception it seems so close to Beckmann's. It may even be identical. But there has been no real meeting of the minds on the issue, and Kostro seems not to know of Beckmann's theory. As to those original quotations, Einstein said 1918 that according to the general theory, space that is considered by the special theory to be empty in fact has physical properties, as follows:

> These are characterized mathematically by the components of the gravitational potential, which describe the metric behavior of this part of space, as well as its gravitational field. This state of things can be easily understood by speaking about an ether, whose state varies continuously from point to point.[4]

The following comment by Kostro plainly attributes the Beckmann thesis to Einstein:

In the years 1918-1926 Einstein used the terms 'physical space' and ether interchangeably, though he preferred to use the latter. He expressed the identity of the gravitational field with the ether, among other things, by referring to the latter as the *gravitational ether*. [5]

Similarly, the eminent mathematician Hermann Weyl, in the 1919 edition of his book on relativity, argued that "the term 'gravitational field' should be replaced by 'ether'."[6]

Lorentz's Role

Einstein's acceptance of a new ether began in 1916. His friend Hendrik Lorentz—Stachel calls him Einstein's "revered father figure"—sent Einstein a long letter about the implications of the general theory. The theory had only recently been published.

In his letter, Lorentz seems to anticipate experimental results 60 years in the future, and discussed in this book. Lorentz's exchanges with Einstein, unearthed by Kostro from the Albert Einstein Archive at Princeton, seem not to have been published in English before.

A "thought experiment" in conjunction with the new general theory had led Lorentz to conclude the following: If "two perfectly conducting wires" were strung around the globe at the equator, and electromagnetic waves transmitted from a starting point A, were sent in opposite directions around the globe, they "will *not* return to A at the same time." The difference between the two "propagation velocities" will necessarily result from "your general formulas," Lorentz told Einstein.[7]

To visualize this, he went on, we can't just think of the Earth, the conducting wires at the equator, and nothing but the "space" or vacuum through which the east- and west-bound waves travel. There's a better way—the way "previously considered to be very natural by all physicists." And that was to envision an ether. Electromagnetic waves propagate in it, and "the propagation velocity relative to the medium is always the same." But there are two reference frames to consider. The rotating Earth is one such, and the ether frame is the other.

"If we start from this point of view," Lorentz continued, "we can say that the experiment has shown us the motion [i.e. the rotation] of the Earth relative to the ether." Therefore, "having recognized the possibility of detecting relative *rotation*, we cannot *a priori* deny the possibility of obtaining the effects of a *translation* of the same kind as well."

The theorized east-west time difference, when electromagnetic signals are sent in opposite directions around the world was verified almost 60 years later, by Ashby and Weiss in 1985. The airborne Hafele-Keating atomic clocks showed the same result.

But Lorentz went astray, surely, when he suggested that, if we can detect a small rotational effect, we can't "*a priori* deny the possibility" of seeing the larger effect of the Earth's translation (orbital motion). Attempts had already been made by Michelson & Co. to detect the large translational effect; without success. Decades later, the smaller rotational effect indeed was detected, thanks to much more refined clocks. But even with more and more accurate instruments investigators still have not been able to detect— and it is safe to say they never will detect—the translational effect. For it isn't there to be seen.

It speaks well of the general theory of relativity, incidentally, and of Lorentz's mathematical skill, that he was able to deduce an effect produced by the Earth's rotation from studying Einstein's field equations, over 50 years before any confirmatory experiment was carried out.

Ten days later Einstein replied to Lorentz. He agreed that his general theory was indeed "closer to the ether hypothesis than the special theory"; also that space once considered "empty" has physical properties characterized by the gravitational potential. But he was not prepared to go all the way with Lorentz; that is, back to the old ether and the physics of the 1880s.[8]

For one thing, readmitting it would restore absolute space and undermine the relativity principle. That was too much for Einstein. In fact, he seemed more concerned at that stage to preserve the relativity principle than the speed of light postulate.

The significant point, however, is that he did accept that space had physical properties expressed by the gravitational field and that this could be called (an) ether. But as it varied from point to point, it could by no means be identified with the old (uniform) ether.

Einstein also did not want to go public with this apparent backsliding right away, Kostro says. "He was too deeply engaged in fighting the old ether to be willing to introduce a new one."[9] He was already under attack by Philipp Lenard for removing the ether in one relativity theory and bringing it back in another. In 1917, Lenard delivered a paper entitled "Relativity Principle, Ether, Gravitation," in which he said that the ether, banished in 1905, "now reappears here with its name changed to 'space.'"

Einstein's reply, published in 1918, took the form of a dialogue with himself. The ether had been "the sick man of theoretical physics," said *The Critic*, and was declared dead in 1905. But, *The Relativist* replied: "It is impossible to say that he is dead now." Nonetheless the old ether, a "system of coordinates at rest" amounted to a "privileged state of motion in the Universe," and that could not be readmitted.[10] Therefore the new ether was not at all the same as the old.

In 1917, Hermann Weyl gave some lectures at the Technical University of Zurich, later incorporated into a book on relativity. His observations were apparently independent of Einstein's. Amidst some technical remarks, Weyl said that "the name 'gravitational field' is perhaps too unilateral," and should "better be replaced by the word 'ether'; while the electromagnetic field should simply be called field." He added that "in reality this ether plays the same role as the ether of the old theory of light ... "[11]

In continuing to oppose the old ether, Einstein adhered to the first postulate of special relativity, which ruled out absolute motion. He seemed unconcerned about the speed-of-light postulate, which the general theory had already undermined.

In an article published in 1911, "On the Influence of Gravitation on Propagation of Light," Einstein acknowledged that the constancy of the velocity of light is "not valid in the formulation which is usually taken as a basis for the ordinary [special] theory of relativity."[12] The velocity of light in the gravitational field "is a function of the place," Einstein said. Light rays "propagated across a gravitational field undergo a deflexion."[13]

Howard Hayden has some interesting thoughts on light's constant velocity. The four-dimensional space-time of general relativity is expressed in the form of metric tensors, one of which uses the symbols $G\mu\nu$. In his letter to Lorentz, Einstein had written: "state of the $G\mu\nu$ = aether." Much complexity hides behind these Greek letters, but Hayden brings it down to the layman's level:

> All this business about $G\mu\nu$ is needed to hold the speed of light constant for all observers. It wouldn't have been necessary to go to all that trouble if Einstein didn't have to preserve a constant speed of light. It would all have been much simpler. The speed of light

would simply depend on where you are in the gravitational field. And that is what Petr Beckmann claims.[14]

This is perhaps the best reason for thinking that Beckmann's theory improves upon Einstein's. A lot of evidence shows that general relativity gives answers that agree with experiment. But it does so by a roundabout method. Einstein's path could have been simpler and more direct if he had not already burdened himself with having to prop up special relativity.

It has been said that Einstein started using the word ether to describe the properties of space out of respect for Lorentz, and stopped doing so after his death in 1928. The attacks by Lenard may have discouraged its use (and encouraged the more obscure "four dimensional space-time.") But Einstein never fully abandoned the word. Visiting Lorentz in Leiden in 1920, he gave a lecture on "Relativity and the Ether." In 1934 he approved the reprinting of this lecture in *The World As I See It*. He further discussed the ether in *The Evolution of Physics*, co-authored with Leopold Infeld (1938). "We may still use the word ether," they wrote,

> but only to express some physical properties of space, The word ether has changed its meaning many times in the development of science. At the moment it no longer stands for a medium built up of particles. Its story, by no means finished, is continued by the relativity theory.[15]

And one final quotation, this from Einstein's 1920 lecture at Leiden. Walter Isaacson used it in his recent biography of Einstein:

> According to the general theory of relativity, space is endowed with physical qualities; in this sense there exists an ether. Space without ether is unthinkable, for in such space there not only would be no propagation of light, but also no possibility of existence for standards of space and time (measuring rods and clocks), nor therefore any spacetime intervals in the physical sense.[16]

Perhaps in the end, then, there really was a meeting of the minds, and a surprising one. Einstein insists that the *relativity* postulate must be retained; and Beckmann is happy to retain it. Einstein and Lorentz differed: should they bring back the old, or a new ether? Beckmann takes Einstein's side. Light rays are deflected by gravity, Einstein says, and Beckmann agrees. When Einstein says that the gravitational potential, whose state varies from point to point, can be regarded as the ether, Beckmann says the same thing, only more simply. He calls it the local gravitational field.

Notes Chapter 21

[1] Ludwik Kostro, *Einstein and the Ether*, Apeiron, Montreal, 2000, p. iii
[2] John Stachel, "Why Einstein Reinvented the Ether," *Physics World*, June 2001.
[3] P.A.M. Dirac, "Is There an Aether?" *Nature,* November 24, 1951.
[4] Kostro, op. cit., p. 76
[5] Kostro, p. 184
[6] Kostro, Jammer foreword, ii
[7] Kostro, p. 66
[8] Kostro, p. 68
[9] Kostro, p. 74
[10] Kostro, p. 76
[11] Kostro, pp.74-75
[12] Kostro, p. 45 Coincidence: the article was written while Einstein was living in Prague. The same principle—that the speed of light is a function of its position in the gravitational field—was reformulated in Prague some 45 later years, in Beckmann's lab.
[13] Einstein, *The Principle of Relativity*, Dover, p. 107.
[14] Author's interview with Howard Hayden, 2005.
[15] *The Evolution of Physics*, Simon & Schuster, 1954, pp. 159-60
[16] W. Isaacson, *Einstein, His Life and Universe*, Simon & Schuster, 2007, p. 318

Chapter 22. Brillet and Hall

I have argued that there was a fringe-shift in the Michelson-Morley experiment, but that it was far too small to have been seen in the 1880s and for decades after that. But it could be seen today, and in fact it may already have been detected.

An experiment in 1979 by Alain Brillet and John L. Hall is said to have been the most precise modern analogue of Michelson-Morley.[1] It was "a tour de force of precision measurement," Howard Hayden wrote. But there was something odd about the design. It looked once more for the effect that Michelson had failed to detect— the "large" effect caused by the Earth's orbital motion. But modern equipment has had no more success in finding it than Michelson's Industrial Age cast iron and mercury flotation. Searching for it once more was like looking for a rock with a microscope, when normal vision had already shown that it didn't exist.

Hall, who won the Nobel Prize for Physics in 2005, is with the Joint Institute for Laboratory Astrophysics at the University of Colorado. Alain Brillet of the University of Paris was then a visiting professor at Boulder. Their experiment was done in Boulder even as Petr Beckmann was teaching there. But he didn't know about it. Hall told me that he had heard of but had never met Beckmann. *Einstein Plus Two* wasn't published until 1987.

Perhaps for the first time, the Brillet-Hall experiment did have the sensitivity to detect the small rotational effect that Beckmann predicted. And they did find an effect, of appropriate magnitude.[2] But Hall was not looking for it. The effect the experimenters saw was assumed to be "spurious"— an experimental error. (In what follows I shall refer simply to Hall, the principal investigator.)

They used the latest equipment and methods—helium-neon laser and Fabry-Perot interferometer on a rotating table. They were trying to detect any "anisotropy" in space. Was it the same in all directions? With the Sun itself moving at an estimated 300 kilometers per second in the direction of the Virgo Cluster, the question was whether any directional effect could be detected.

But why should it be seen? If the gravitational field is carried with the Earth one should not expect any such large effect to appear. Nonetheless a small fringe shift was detected.

The apparatus was rotated in the laboratory, just as Michelson's was. The experimenters wanted to see is if any shift in the fringes was associated with any particular direction in space. With the interferometer pointed toward Virgo, for example, was the position of the fringes any different? But no directional effect was found.

But Brillet and Hall did find "a spurious nearly sinusoidal frequency shift at the table-rotation rate." This is what Petr Beckmann would have expected, given relative motion between the rotating Earth and its field. No earlier experiment had ever had the sensitivity to show it.

This apparent fringe shift was unrelated to any particular direction with respect to the stars. It appeared at any time of the day, simply keeping time with the table rotation rate. For that reason, the experimenters concluded that it was unrelated to the Earth's motion in space. Hall wasn't thinking of an ether-wind as a function of the Earth's rotation either, so the effect didn't seem important.

At 40 degrees latitude, the Earth's rotational velocity is about 350 meters per second. The frequency shift was of approximately the right magnitude. In his paper, however, Hall interpreted it as having been caused by "the varying gravitational stretching" of the apparatus itself, perhaps because the axis of the rotating table was not "perfectly vertical." But that was a guess, he said.

Howard Hayden analyzed the experiment in a paper published by *Physics Essays*, "Is the Velocity of Light Isotropic in the Frame of the Rotating Earth?" Although he found that the "spurious" effect was close in magnitude to what Beckmann's theory predicted, it seemed to be "off" directionally by about 30 degrees.[3]

A few independent researchers have contacted John Hall since 1979 and asked him about this "spurious" effect. To one he replied: "The observed signal fixed in the laboratory frame may possibly be real, due to any of several possibilities. For one, the experiment was conducted very near to one wall in a large underground lab: this writes a clear gravitational gradient into our space."

Dennis J. McCarthy, an independent biogeographer, wrote to Hall: "I am interested in the possibility that the signal may not have been due to an instrument effect at all—but due to an anisotropy of space with respect to the lab frame caused by the rotation of the Earth." McCarthy suggested repeating the experiment nearer the equator, where the Earth's rotational velocity would be higher. Would the anomaly increase commensurately?

"You propose a concrete and good experiment," Hall replied. Hall had considered redoing the experiment, incorporating other changes. But as we shall see, there was an unexpected problem with the equipment.

Plainly, the experiment should be redone, but with a different theory in mind. The problem has been "the sidereal fixation" of the experimentalists, Hayden said. "As long as they concentrate on determining the velocity of the Earth through the cosmos, they are blind to the other question."

Hayden says he knows of no other experiments that have attempted to detect the effect of the Earth's rotation, not counting his own repetition of the (1909) Trouton-Noble experiment.

In September and again in October, 2004, I interviewed Dr. Hall, with a view to revisiting these questions. Could the "spurious" effect found in Brillet and Hall have been the effect that Petr Beckmann expected to find? [4]

Hall replied that he was "very much involved in trying to get this question solved." But by now he had the following problem. "Regrettably," he said, the rotation apparatus that he used in 1979 "had taken up space that we could no longer spare." He obtained federal storage space and figured he would get his apparatus back. But it was stored in the Rocky Mountain Arsenal, "in the place where they made nerve gas." So the officials declined to return it.

"Under the circumstances I guess I don't want it," Hall said. Anyway he no longer had access to it when I spoke to him.

I asked him about the problem raised by the 30-degree angular displacement. In Beckmann's theory, the observed effect "should cluster around angles corresponding to the compass points," Hayden wrote. But the experimenters had failed to describe "the orientation of their apparatus with respect to the compass."

Hall said this was not a problem. He never had been able to properly reconstruct from their data the compass point at which the effect was observed. The problem was that they had very little computer memory. There was also a "continuous frequency drift, apparently caused by some kind of expansion of the material." So they experimented with different rotation rates and in the end the data from their different runs was not coordinated with respect to the compass points. So it's possible that the effect they saw was oriented as Hayden had expected and not astray by 30 degrees.

Hayden was relieved to hear that. It meant that the effect was not necessarily a falsification of Beckmann's theory. In fact, the difficulties that Hall encountered give just one more reason why the experiment should be repeated.

By 2004, Hall was indeed trying a new experiment. But because he no longer had the old equipment, he was using a different design that has become all too common. It uses the Earth's own daily rotation to sweep the apparatus slowly across the heavens over a 24-hour period. This method appeals to experimentalists because the Earth's rotation is vibration-free, obviating the need for motors. It gives experimenters greater sensitivity.

But it also meant that Hall was *not* redoing Brillet-Hall, because the interferometer was no longer rotating in the lab. His design now meant that he would only be able detect a light-speed differential with respect to the stars—an "anisotropy of space." That is also what he was looking for in 1979. He could then also have seen a rotational effect, but that is no longer possible.

If we are to detect the slow "ether wind" passing through the laboratory because the Earth is rotating on its axis, the apparatus must rotate in the lab, as it did in Michelson-Morley.

I asked Dennis McCarthy if he knew of more recent experiments with rotating equipment. "As far as I am aware, in every new test, they are obtaining greater accuracy with larger, blockier instruments that are cemented to the floor," he replied. "They are not rotating the apparatus in the lab frame. So they can't find any effects due to the Earth's rotation—only orbital effects that Michelson-Morley showed weren't there in 1887."[5]

The problem is this. If a faint ether wind is blowing all around the world thanks to the Earth's rotation, you cannot use the Earth's rotation to detect it. The measured effect will be a constant, with nothing to compare it to. You must rotate the interferometer within the lab, so that you can compare the speed of the reflected light beam with that of a beam at right angles to it. Michelson's experimental design is needed, only with vastly greater sensitivity. Hall had the sensitivity, but he no longer has the equipment. And he hasn't been working with the right theory either.

Imagine you are standing in a flat-bed truck open to the wind, holding a toy propeller as the truck drives forward. The truck's motion causes a wind which turns the propeller. The truck drives in a big circle of a mile radius and returns to its starting point. You look to see if that backward breeze is associated with any particular compass point, and of course it isn't. The propeller keeps on whirling without change. Only if you, standing in the back of the truck, were to turn around through 360 degrees on the spot, would you realize that the breeze was associated with a particular direction—namely (in this instance) the front of the truck.

As long as the interferometer is always pointed in the same direction within the lab, no speed differential associated with the Earth's rotation can be detected.

As far as I know, all the sophisticated experiments today use interferometers that are fixed to the floor. All retain the "sidereal fixation" that Hayden mentioned. All rely on the Earth's rotation to ensure that the interferometer simply sweeps through the heavens at a rate of 15 degrees per hour.

I asked Hall if he would expect to see an effect caused by the Earth's rotation, provided he could retrieve his old apparatus and re-do his old experiment. He has no doubt that such an effect is present, he told me. Here he introduced an interesting new twist.

"What we know and believe is that general relativity tells us that there is curvature in our local space," he said. And because we're on the surface of the Earth, he felt "completely sure that there is some effect," and "numerically it comes out to something that is rather similar to what was seen."

He was saying, in other words, that general relativity already predicts that there should be a visible effect caused by the Earth's rotation. Lorentz had said the same thing to Einstein in 1916.

"We tell our students that the world is one way," Hall went on. But then, when we go into the laboratory it isn't. "The laboratory is on a spinning ball. If you turn up the sensitivity, it's completely sure that you will see these things. So then the statement that you can't discover what your state of inertia is by internal experiments is false in principle. Although it is approximately valid."

He seemed to be questioning the relativity principle itself. It's an interesting thought.

In other words it is possible that inside a railroad car that is stationary with respect to the tracks, a Michelson interferometer can be sensitive enough to show that it is moving (with respect to the gravitational field). The interferometer would be rotating along with the globe, and therefore "through" the Earth's field. This should produce a fringe shift just as Beckmann had predicted. And Hall may have already detected it.

If such an experiment *does* unambiguously show an effect, and of the magnitude expected from the Earth's rotation, the argument we shall probably hear is that *of course* there is such a fringe shift— and general relativity predicts it. For that is how the Einsteinians already responded, to the Michelson-Gale experiment and the others already described. And general relativity does indeed predict such an effect. But there was an easier way.

Notes Chapter 22

[1] A. Brillet and J. L. Hall, "Improved Laser Test of the Isotropy of Space," *Physical Review Letters*, v. 42, 26 February, 1979, pp. 549-552.

[2] Howard C. Hayden, "Is the Velocity of Light Isotropic in the Frame of the Rotating Lab? *Physics Essays*, v. 4, 1991, p. 364; and "Special Relativity: Problems and Alternatives," *Physics Essays*, v. 8, no. 3, 1995, p. 372

[3] Howard Hayden, *Physics Essays*, 1991, pp. 361-367.

[4] Author's interviews with John L. Hall, September and October, 2004.

[5] Author's interview with Dennis McCarthy, April 2004.

Chapter 23. A Historical Parallel

There is a historical parallel, and in its repercussions it may have been as important as the search for Michelson's fringe shift. I refer to the search for stellar parallax in earlier centuries. The undetected ether led to the theory of relativity. The undetected stellar parallax for many years delayed acceptance of the Copernican theory.

The search for a shift in the fringes in Michelson's interferometer continued for 50 years before it was abandoned by the principals. The most important was Michelson's successor at the Case School, Dayton C. Miller. In fact, with added refinements, investigations sporadically persisted until the centenary of the original experiment. As for the search for stellar parallax, it was actively pursued from the 16th until the 19th century. It did not end until the 1830s, when the tiny displacement in the positions of the nearest stars was finally discovered.

The ancients understood that the sun is indeed many millions of miles away. So the Earth's orbital diameter must be huge. The stars, in a given position at a certain time of the year, should appear in slightly different alignments six months later. The line of sight would change for all the stars, but more so for those closer to us. Range-finders, with two telescopes a fixed distance apart, operate on the same principle.

Tycho Brahe, the 16th century Danish nobleman and astronomer who was wealthy enough to build his own observatory and hire Kepler as his assistant, was unable to detect stellar parallax. It was the reason he gave for rejecting the Copernican theory. Copernicus meanwhile had accepted the correct explanation: the stars were much further away than anyone imagined. In contrast, Tycho thought the stars were located "just beyond Saturn."

"Much of his unwillingness to accept Copernicanism stemmed …from his inability to imagine that God would have created a universe containing as much wasted space as the Copernican system and the absence of annual parallax required," wrote Tycho's biographer. "If there were no other absurdities in the Copernican system, the necessity of assuming such a vast distance to the stars would be enough to rule it out," said Tycho.[1]

The first task that Kepler set himself was to confirm the Earth's motion around the sun by proving the existence of stellar parallax. He expected a shift of half a degree in the position of the Pole Star, as seen after six months, and his instruments were accurate enough to detect that. "But there was no variation; the starry sky remained immutable."[2]

The prolonged inability to detect parallax did not prevent but surely did delay acceptance of the heliocentric system. It led also to unnecessarily complicated solar-system models, such as Tycho's, in which the Earth was at the center and the planets orbited the Sun.

In the same way, I have argued, the inability to detect a small shift in the position of optical fringes in the 1880s led to a reconstruction of physics in the 20th century that was unnecessarily complicated.

This issue was discussed by Stanley Goldberg. After the Copernican system was proposed, anti-Copernicans called for the evidence for stellar parallax, which had never been observed. "There was no empirical evidence that would give anyone, except those already committed for other reasons, confidence in the heliocentric theory," Goldberg wrote. "Heliocentric astronomy gained acceptance in the absence of evidence."

When parallax was at last discovered, there was no mention that the Copernican theory was now confirmed. "The reason is clear," Goldberg concluded. "The discovery occurred long after the theory had been accepted. And the acceptance of the theory had little to do with that kind of evidence. The same thing happened to the theory of relativity. There was no empirical evidence."[3]

Goldberg of course puts his own spin on the parallel. It is not quite true that "there was no empirical evidence" for relativity, for there was Michelson's experiment. But relativity brought with it great difficulties and complications, including the revision of Newton's laws. If simplicity was its justification, simplicity was not achieved. One is even inclined to say that the new theory was Ptolemaic in its complexity.

Furthermore, the Copernicans had several reasons for adopting a theory that really did simplify astronomy. As far as I can see, the relativists had little reason to adopt a theory that greatly complicated physics. Overall, the comparison suggests that the Renaissance and Enlightenment astronomers were less hasty than modern physicists in coming to a conclusion based on one anomalous observation.

"Eventually the true parallaxes of some of the nearer stars were observed," Abell, Morrison and Wolff write in *Realm of the Universe*.

> The first successful detections were in the year 1838, when Friedrich Bessel (Germany) Thomas Henderson (Cape of Good Hope) and Friedrich Struve (Russia) measured the parallaxes of the stars 61 Cygni, Alpha Centauri and Vega respectively. However, even the nearest star, Alpha Centauri, showed a total displacement of only about 1.5 arc-sec during the year. Small wonder that Tycho Brahe was unable to observe the stellar parallaxes and concluded that the Earth was stationary.[4]

Notice how far off the early astronomers were. The half-degree parallax that Kepler expected to find was 1800 seconds of arc. The actual parallax of 61 Cygni discovered by Bessel was 0.3 seconds of arc. In other words, Kepler and others (some expected an even larger displacement) were looking for something at least 6000 times larger than it turned out to be.

Michelson was looking for an effect 10,000 times too large. So the respective errors were of the same order of magnitude.

Parallels and Contrasts

Howard Hayden said that physicists would tell him that "relativity works," and they would stick with it as long as it works. It gave the right results, in other words. One might say that it continued to work as long as their clocks remained relatively insensitive. The relativistic departure from the classical predictions was a matter of nanoseconds and it wasn't until the development of atomic clocks that these tiny slivers of time could be measured. And that didn't happen until the 1970s. When it did happen, the Hafele-Keating measurements (and others since) were immediately in conflict with special relativity.

Analogously, it took a long time (centuries) before telescopes were sensitive enough to confirm the Copernican theory.

There are also sharp contrasts. The hunt for stellar parallax was constructive, whereas (for reasons that should now be clear) the search for the Michelson fringe shift became increasingly futile.

The search for parallax yielded important discoveries, among them binary stars. At the end of the 18th century Sir William Herschel found many examples of closely aligned stars, which he thought would demonstrate parallax. But they turned out to be binaries, circling one another in accordance with Newton's and Kepler's laws. And this gave cosmologists reason to believe that "the whole universe is governed by the same natural laws."[5]

In contrast, Dayton Miller's protracted search seems forlorn. He spent the next 40 years, on and off, looking for a fringe shift based on the Earth's orbital motion. His passion for music and his interest in acoustics and sound waves convinced him that light is fully analogous to sound (a reasonable enough idea). As late as 1925 he was still repeating Michelson-Morley and even reporting that he had found a fringe shift.[6]

Others kept looking. Auguste Piccard repeated the experiment from the gondola of a balloon in 1926 but failed to detect anything.[7] Louis Essen tried again in 1955 with short radio waves. He worked for Britain's National Physical Laboratory and later published a pamphlet attacking special relativity.[8] He nonetheless concluded that Dayton Miller's findings were incorrect.[9] The last attempt reported by Loyd Swenson was that of Charles H. Townes in 1963. Using a maser (which he invented), he failed to find a fringe shift.

Of course, Miller and his successors had embraced the wrong theory. They were following in Michelson's footsteps, even as Michelson himself had turned in a more productive direction. The key lay in the Earth's rotational, not its orbital motion.

One might say that Herschel was right to search for parallax and all he needed was more accurate instruments; and Michelson was right to search for an ether and all *he* needed was more accurate instruments. But the parallel breaks down, in that Herschel's underlying picture of the Copernican system was correct while Michelson's picture of the luminiferous medium was initially incorrect. It had to be changed. Dayton Miller and his successors were never able to grasp that change. And to be fair, Michelson was not always clear about these matters himself.

It isn't until we come to Peter Beckmann's *Einstein Plus Two* that we find a clear statement of the new theory: the ether is synonymous with the local gravitational field. Therefore the Earth's diurnal rotation should produce a fringe-shift. But it would be four orders of magnitude smaller than anticipated.

An immediate deduction from a light medium that does not rotate with the Earth is a difference in the speed of light, to the east and west. This has been detected, by Hafele and Keating, and in the around-the-world Sagnac experiment. The Michelson-Gale experiment of 1924 confirmed that the Earth's rotation did produce a fringe shift. But because the rotating Earth is non-inertial, it was disqualified as a refutation of special relativity. But because of the Earth's spherical shape and perpetual rotation, the same argument could be used against all Earth-bound experiments.

If that indeed is to be the response, special relativity should be considered an unfalsifiable theory—and rejected as such.

A new experiment using the original Michelson-Morley design and much greater accuracy might pass muster. I once read somewhere that Einstein accepted that if Michelson-Morley showed a fringe shift then it would falsify special relativity. But I have never been able to find it again, despite much hunting.

What is needed is a repeat of John Hall's experiment. It had sufficient accuracy in 1979, so someone should be able to reproduce it 30 years on. The experiment did show a signal consistent with a "rotational" fringe shift but it was not expected, and discounted as spurious. I hope that younger experimenters may undertake this task. The challenge could be considerable, but the intellectual consequences great.

Einstein's Priority?

I spent much of the book saying that, contrary to the accepted interpretation, Einstein's special theory of relativity is incorrect, and unhelpful. Then Einstein found a way to resolve these problems with his general theory. But he took a difficult and complex route—

the complexity having been dictated by his continuing fidelity to the special theory, which he wanted to preserve.

With Beckmann's *Einstein Plus Two* the identity between the ether and the gravitational field is plainly formulated, but there's a final irony. As we have seen there was one man who had already recognized how the ether should be construed. His name was Albert Einstein. It may well have been his earlier repudiation of the ether that prevented him from more forcefully stating how it should be revived. Nonetheless, it is amazing to realize that Einstein saw and for a number of years stated that the ether and the local gravitational field are effectively the same.

So perhaps Einstein can claim priority, in this as in so many other things. Petr Beckmann was a good friend, and I doubt if he knew about Einstein's ruminations about the ether and the gravitational field. It is little known to this day. But if Beckmann were alive now, I'm sure he would be delighted to read what Einstein wrote on the subject. He might even have been happy to acknowledged Einstein's priority, if that were expected and appropriate. Considerations of priority, for Petr, were insignificant compared to his search for the truth.

Notes Chapter 23

[1] Victor E. Thoren, *The Lord of Uraniborg, A Biography of Tycho Brahe,* Cambridge, 1990, p. 304
[2] Arthur Koestler, *The Sleepwalkers*, The Macmillan Co., 1968, p. 276
[3] Stanley Goldberg, *Understanding Relativity*, pp. 148-49
[4] Abell, Morrison and Wolff, *Realm of the Universe, 4ᵗʰ* ed. Saunders, 1988, p. 262.
[5] Abell, Morrison op. cit., p. 262
[6] Loyd Swenson, *Ethereal Aether*, p. 210
[7] Swenson, op. cit., p. 215
[8] Louis Essen, *The Special Theory of Relativity: A Critical Analysis*, Oxford, 1971
[9] Swenson, op. cit., p. 241

Chapter 24. Synopsis

If the argument of this book is correct then the special theory of relativity will eventually have to be discarded. An inertial reference frame, which is required if any experiment is to qualify as a test of that theory, is little more than a polite fiction. The Earth is a spinning ball, so any experiment conducted on its surface is unavoidably subject to inertial forces. This potentially disqualifies any experiment as a legitimate test of the special theory, and in practice does disqualify it if experimental results conflict with the predictions of that theory. It is then treated as a test of general relativity, which takes the gravitational field into account.

The special theory declared the ether to be superfluous and the speed of light to be a constant, whatever the motion of the light source or observer. In the Michelson-Gale experiment (1925), which was sensitive enough to detect the effect of the rotating Earth on the speed of light, a fringe shift was seen. So the experiment was treated as non-inertial and not a valid refutation of the special theory. Instead it was regarded as corroborating the general theory.

Before Einstein, physicists had regarded the light-bearing medium, or ether, as filling the whole of space uniformly. Petr Beckmann posited that the luminiferous medium is not uniform but is equivalent to the local gravitational field, which becomes ever more attenuated with distance from the gravitating body. Light rays entering denser regions of this field are deflected slightly and travel more slowly, in accordance with Fermat's Principle, or with Snell's Law. Using a different and more complicated approach, general relativity makes the same prediction.

The gravitational field of the Earth moves "through" the laboratory, and does so at the rotational velocity of the Earth. As the field of the eastward rotating Earth passes through the lab, the speed of light is observed to be slightly higher east to west than it is west to east. When atomic clocks were transported to the east and west in the Hafele-Keating experiment, just such an east-west clock differential was observed.

This contradicts the claim of the special theory that the speed of light is the same in all directions. The speed of light, constant by postulate, is not constant by experiment. Special relativity also predicts that time in moving reference frames is dilated: moving clocks run slowly. But in Hafele-Keating it was found that, when transported by jet planes to the east, clocks slow down, compared to stationary clocks, while those flown to the west speed up.

This anomaly, papered over by referring the motion of transported clocks to an Earth-centered inertial reference frame, seemed to give results roughly consistent with relativity. But it did so at the cost of abandoning a cardinal rule of relativity, that there shall be no preferred reference frames. The same adjustment was made with GPS clocks. Their corrections are said to be relativistic but they also invoke the same preferred reference frame.

The ability of atomic clocks to measure time in billionths of a second seems to be forcing physicists to abandon special relativity in practice. Observed east-west differentials have plainly demonstrated that *clocks* slow down when they traverse a gravitational field, but this is not the same as the relativistic claim that *time* slows down when an observer moves with respect to a clock.

Observation from the reference frame of accelerated particles, or from muons in space, should (according to the special theory) show spatial contraction and time dilation in the outside world. But no observations from such a vantage point have yet been made. As for the length contraction predicted by special relativity since 1905, and demonstrated graphically in many books, it has never been observed.

The general theory, sometimes called a theory of gravity, does seem to give results that agree with experiment. But it does so by a roundabout route. Additional complications were built into the theory because Einstein and his followers wanted to preserve the special theory of relativity intact. That required additional mathematical steps and assumptions.

Nonetheless, by 1911 Einstein had already accepted that "the velocity of light in the gravitational field is a function of the place [in that field]," and "undergoes deflexion." Therefore it does not travel at a constant speed. This became central to his general theory. If Einstein had started out with his general theory and had early on accepted that the local gravitational field is equivalent to the ether, his theory would have been much simpler and perhaps indistinguishable from Beckmann's.

For a number of years Einstein did accept that the gravitational field, varying from point to point, could be regarded as an ether— though not the same as the classical ether. His new ether seems to have been the same as Beckmann's in practice. But he was uncomfortable with bringing it back, even in a new incarnation, because he had already so conspicuously dispensed with the old ether in 1905. Again, his prior commitment to special relativity seems to have obstructed the path toward a simplification of his later (general) theory.

If the local gravitational field is the ether that Michelson-Morley looked for, then the fringe shift that they could not detect in 1887 should be present, but (in mid latitudes) four orders of magnitude smaller than they expected. The most accurate such interferometer experiment yet performed may have detected an effect of the magnitude predicted by Beckmann, but the experimenters were not looking for it and viewed it as "spurious."

That experiment, by Brillet and Hall (1979), should be repeated. If a fringe shift is unambiguously shown, then physicists will have to decide whether the special theory has been falsified or whether the effect (once again) can be attributed to the non-inertial nature of all Earth-bound experiments. Howard Hayden has suggested they could also re-do the experiment on the space shuttle, which should produce a larger fringe shift because of its much higher speed through the gravitational field.

On the astronomical scale, the stellar aberration exhibited by binary stars seems to falsify special relativity. Einstein's theory predicts that stellar aberration is a function of the relative motion of the star and an observer on Earth. Therefore the aberration of spectroscopic binaries should wax and wane in sync with the period of their orbits. But the aberration of orbiting binary stars remains a constant—unaffected by their motion with respect to the observer.

-----◇-----

INDEX

Aberration, stellar, xxi-xxii, 53,
  87-92, 96-101, 103
Abraham, Max, 111
Accelerators, particle, 73-75
  Mesons/muons, 125-28
Ashby-Allan-Weiss experiment,
  xvi, 146, 181
Ashby, Neil, 144, 147, 149, 150
Asimov, Isaac, 49
Atomic clocks, key role in testing
  special relativity, 134, 138,
  144, 150, 193

Baierlein, Ralph, 69, 77, 78, 82-
  84, 133
Beckmann, Petr, vii-x, xii-xxi, 1,
  9, 17, 26, 42, 45, 74, 79, 82,
  91, 100-01, 104-08, 113-14,
  128, 130, 140, 147, 163-166,
  172, 187, 190, 196
  theory of, xiv, xx, 26, 62, 92,
    103-108, 157, 195
  and Michelson-Gale, xvi, 92,
    105, 118, 123
  prediction on particle
    experiments, 130
  and Paul Gerber, 172, 174-75
  and Brillet-Hall, 185-89, 190
  and Einstein's new ether, 106,
    179, 183-84, 195-96
Bernstein, Jeremy, 31, 68, 78,
  145, 165
Binary stars, x, xxi, 61, 92-93,
  95, 194
  see spectroscopic binaries, 95-
    102
Bradley, James, 53, 56, 87-88,
  90, 95-96

Brahe, Tycho, 191-92
Brillet-Hall experiment, xv, 185-
  90
Brown, G. Burniston, 79-80

Clark, Ronald, 78, 90
Clemens, J. Christopher, 175

Dicke, R. H. 154
Dingle, Herbert, 48
Dirac, Paul, 48, 179
Doppler Effect, xxi, 87, 92, 96-
  97, 99, 100, 128

$E=mc^2$, vii, xi, xix, 1, 63, 77-85
East-west asymmetry of c, see
  Light speed
Eddington, A. 32, 68, 70, 121,
  164, 167, 175-77, 179
Eisner, Edward, 99
Eotvos, Roland von, 154
Essen, Louis, 194
Ether, xiii-xiv, 7-9, 19-23, 25-28,
  31-35, 38-39, 41-44, 50, 54,
  61-62, 63-64, 89-90, 92, 120,
  186, 188
  entrained ether, xiv, 26-27, 89-
    90
  equivalent to gravitational
    field, xviii, 74-75, 101, 103-
    07, 113-14, 118, 162, 172,
    195-96
  Einstein's revival of, 1, 35,
    105-06, 179-84
  Maxwellian ether, 7, 19-20,
    27, 63
Everitt, Francis, 16, 17

Faraday, Michael, 53, 59, 62
Fermat's Principle, 113, 163-64,
   167
Fermi, Enrico, 126
Fizeau, Armand, 53, 56
Flandern, Thomas Van, 176-77
Folsing, Albrecht, 78, 171, 174
Frank, Philipp, 78, 90
French, A. P. 62, 65, 90, 128,
   137
Fresnel, Augustin, 89, 111

Gale, Henry G. 25, 117-18, 121,
   123
Galilean transformation, 46,
   Galileo, 5-6, 79
Galison, Peter, 143, 149
Gamow, George, 83-84, 125-27,
   158
Gardner, Martin, 78, 158
General Relativity, 1, 4, 15-17,
   107, 110, 113 120-21, 153-59,
   161-69, 171-78
   comes to rescue of special
      relativity, 107, 112, 120
   equivalence principle, and,
      153-155
   gravitational lensing, 168
   gravitational red shift, 164-65
   Mercury's orbit, 171-78
   complexity of, dictated by
      adherence to Special
      Relativity, 113-14, 169,
      182-83, 195-96
   Shapiro time delay, 166-67
Gehrcke, E. 172-73
Gerber, Paul, 172-178
Global Positioning System, 1,
   109, 129, 138, 143-51
Goldberg, Stanley, 34, 83, 111,
   192
Gravity Probe B, 163

Gravity, speed of, 175-77

Habicht, Conrad, 81, 171
Hafele-Keating, xvi-xviii, 133-
   41, 146, 148, 181, 193
Hafele, J. C. 133-35, 138-39
Hale, George, 27, 55, 117
Hall, John, 105, 185-90, 195
Hasenohrl, Fritz, 81
Hayden, Howard, xiii-xxii, 98-
   101, 106-07, 109, 137, 140,
   150, 157, 163, 175, 177, 182-
   83, 186-88, 193
Hawking, Steven, x, 63, 134
Heaviside, Oliver, 62
Hecht, Eugene, 114-15
Helmholtz, Herman, 22-23, 80
Herschel, William, 95, 194
Hoffmann, B. 11-12, 22, 32, 40-
   43, 78, 88, 129-30
Holton, Gerald, 19, 28, 51-58,
   59, 72, 90
Huygens, C. 111, 156

Infeld, Leopold, 31, 54, 67, 183
Isaacson, Walter, 78, 106, 179,
   183
Ives, Herbert, 96, 99, 128
Ives-Stilwell, 128

Jaffe, Bernard, 55
Jammer, Max, 71, 74, 78, 106,
   179
Joule, James P. 80

Kaufmann, W. 69, 72
Kelvin, Lord, 26, 28, 79
Kepler, Johannes, 99, 191-92,
   193, 194
Kostro, Ludwik, 106, 179-81
Kox, A. J. 31
Krauss, Lawrence, 153-54

Larmor, Joseph, 28, 123, 128
Laue, Max von, 53, 174
Lemon, Harvey, 119, 122
Lenard, Philip, 181, 183
Lewis, Gilbert, 69, 73-74, 77, 81-82
Light rays, bending of, 161-169
Light Speed, c,
    constant by postulate, xiii,
        34,37-40,42,45,48,50,60
    not constant by experiment,
        118, 139-40, 156, 181-82
    east-west asymmetry of, x-
        xvii, 118, 135, 139-40, 181
    constancy implied by Maxwell
        equations, 62-65
    Beckmann-Hayden wager re
        constancy, ix, xvii, 140
Lightman, Alan, 6, 9, 78
Livingston, Dorothy Michelson,
    27-29, 121-22
Lodge, Oliver, 123
Lorentz, Hendrik A, 24, 26, 31-
    36, 45, 47, 55, 72, 73, 105,
    128, 129, 180-81, 183
Lorentz transformations, 45, 47,
    48, 74, 77

Mach, Ernst, 70, 173
Magellan, Ferdinand, 113-14
Magie, William F. 53
Mass, increase with velocity, 67-
    76
Maxwell, James Clerk, 7, 8, 16,
    19-20, 22, 64-65
Maxwell equations, 2, 60, 62-65,
    81
Mayer, Julius, 80
McCarthy, Dennis, 186-87, 188
McCormmach, R. 34
Mercury's orbit, see General
    Relativity
Mermin, N. David, 12

Mesons/muons, 125-28
Michelson, Albert, xiii- xx, 9,
    19-30, 35, 64-65, 89, 91-92,
    105, 115, 119-22,
    some Michelson papers
        discarded, 27-28
    his views on entrained ether,
        xiv, 89-91, 115, 117
    and Einstein, 28-29, 105-06
Michelson-Gale experiment,
    xvi, xx, 91-92, 105, 107,
    115, 117-24, 157, 190
    New York Times and, 122
Michelson-Morley, xx, 8, 9,
    16, 17, 19-30, 31, 35, 49,
    51-58, 62, 65, 89-90, 104,
    115, 192-94, 195
    Einstein's disputed early
        knowledge of, 51-57
Millikan, Robert, 54, 55
Miller, Arthur I., 32, 51, 57, 127-
    28, 129
Miller, Dayton C, 25, 26, 27, 55,
    191, 194
Mizar A (star in Big Dipper), 95-
    96, 98-99
Morley, Edward, 24
Mossbauer, R. 165
Motion through field slows
    clocks, not time, 49, 128-129,
    137, 145, 165

Newcomb, Simon, 20, 171
Newton, Isaac, 6, 71-72, 79, 88,
    97, 154, 162, 171, 175-76, 177

Pais, Abraham, 55, 56, 78, 125,
    162, 171-72
Park, David, 129
Parker, Barry, 67-68, 78
Pauli, Wolfgang, 112, 174
Phipps, Thomas, 99-100
Pickering, Edward, 95

Planck, Max, 51
Poincaré, Henri, 28, 33-34, 48,
    69-70, 72, 111
Pokorny, Jiri, 104
Post, E. J. 111-12
Pound, R. V. and Rebka, G.
    experiment, 165
Powell, Corey, 12, 60
Preferred reference frame,
    see Special Relativity
Ritz, Walter, 61-62, 98
Rogers, Eric, 11, 83
Rothman, Tony, 95, 100-101
Rutherford, Ernest, 81

Sagnac experiment, Sagnac
    effect, xv, xx, 107, 109-16,
    118, 120, 123, 149, 157, 195
Sartori, Leo, 23, 28, 33, 34, 38,
    40, 72, 78, 90, 126, 133, 144-
    46
Schiff, Leonard, 163, 166
Seeliger, H. von, 174
Serber, Robert, 83
Shankland, Robert S, 55, 119,
    120, 122
Shapiro, Irwin, time-delay
    experiment, 161, 166-67
Silberstein, L. 121-22
Sitter, Willem de, 61, 98
Snell's Law, 162
Soldner, J. G. von, 162
Sommerfeld, A. 171
Space and time, deformation of,
    in special relativity, 13, 32, 34,
    35, 43-47, 52, 53, 60, 65, 67,
    73
Special Relativity, ix, xiii, 1-4, 8,
    12-13, 37-50, 52, 54, 61, 106,
    120, 127-28
    Earth-centered inertial frame,
    and, 135, 138, 147-48

Einstein's emendation of, 111,
    136, 140, 148, 150, 182
escape route into general
    relativity, xvi, xix-xx, 107,
    120, 122, 156-57, 190
falsified by aberration of
    binary stars, 92-93, 95-101
inertial ref. frame, unreality of,
    107, 140, 189, 195
revolutionary character of, 9,
    41, 47-48, 51, 53, 57
peculiar difficulty of, 9-10, 11-
    16
preferred ref. frame forbidden
    by, 46, 68, 75, 127
preferred ref. frame accepted
    by, 138, 147, 150
seeks to simplify, but
    complicates physics, 8-9,
    69, 169, 192-93
thought experiments,
    questionable use of, 60
Stachel, John, 56, 59, 77, 179-80
Stellar aberration, see Aberration
Stellar parallax, 87, 95, 191-194
Stokes, George, 90-91
Swenson, Loyd, 24-25, 30, 58,
    93, 124, 194

Tangerlini, Frank, 162
Teller, Edward, 17, 106, 108, 158
Terrell, James, 129
Thorne, Kip S., xvi, 51
Tian, R. and Lee, Z. xviii, 163
Todd, D. P. 64
Townes, Charles H. 194
Trouton-Noble experiment, xviii,
    187

Weyl, Hermann, 180, 182
White and Gribbin (biog.), 78;
    Gribbin, J. and M., 63
Whitney, Cynthia Kolb, x, 109

Whittaker, Edmund, 33, 77
Will, Clifford, ix, 78, 135, 143,
    167
Wolfson, Richard, 5, 168-69

Young, Thomas, 22, 89

Zee, A. 155
Zwicky, Fritz, 168

The Author

A graduate of Oxford University, Tom Bethell came to the U.S. and became a journalist and writer. He has published books on a range of subjects from the benefits of private property to New Orleans jazz. He has also been a media fellow at the Hoover Institution, Stanford. Petr Beckmann stimulated his interest in relativity and the possibility that it could be understood in a new way. After Petr's death, Howard C. Hayden added greatly to that understanding.

Vales Lake Publishing

Vales Lake Publishing
P.O. Box 7609
Pueblo West, CO 81007-0609
(719) 547-7805
fax: (719) 547-7819
SAN: 2 5 4—2 5 3

Please visit www.valeslake.com to obtain books on energy, climate, mathematics, probability, relativity, electromagnetic radiation, and beaded jewelry. We have numerous *Golem Press* books written by, and translated by the late Petr Beckmann.

We also publish the monthly energy newsletter *The Energy Advocate*. Please contact us for a sample.